Ireland's Magdalen

Teresa [signature]

Teresa Marie Fee

Ireland's Magdalen

COPYRIGHT 2008

By: Teresa Marie Fee Goodman

ISBN: 978-0-692-82884-7

Library of Congress Control Number: 2017941859

Another Fine Literary Work by:
(ALCHEMY STUDIO INC Est. 1970)

www.alchemystudioinc.com

This book is, in all essentials, FACTUAL.

The names of people are actual.

The places are real.

The dates have not been changed.

The incidents are founded on truth.

FOREWORD

Ireland is a land of legend, and the Irish are known worldwide as storytellers and singers, both sweet and sorrowful.

Allow me the benefit of a few words about the book you are about to read. The first time I read *Ireland's Magdalen* was in front of the Veterans Hospital in Lebanon, Pennsylvania. I began reading while sitting in my car, having arrived early for a dental appointment. As I read, I found myself racing the clock on the dashboard, glancing toward the back of the chapter to see how many pages were left. I felt that I had to finish Chapter Two before my appointment, or it would have plagued me during those long periods in the dental chair. I finished the chapter at the expense of being late for the appointment.
The doctor was not pleased or amused by my excuse.

Over a period of twenty-five years, Teresa Fee has asked me to accompany her on travels to Ireland for research on this book. At times, I felt like I was just one step above a ghoul, as she had me traipsing around cemeteries all over Ireland, looking for the family tombstone and the inscriptions it may contain.

The story I am about to relate is absolutely true. Anyone who knows me personally would tell you that I am a rather stoic businessman, not one inclined toward the fantastic or fantasy of any sort. I could care less about the aliens at "Area 51" or anywhere else for that matter, but this tale still sends shivers up my spine.

We were traveling in the far northern regions of County Mayo, Ireland. After having spent a delightful evening at a B&B in the small town north of Ballina, the next morning, over breakfast, we inquired of the owner about old cemeteries in the region. Parish records are a prerequisite for family research in Ireland. She pointed out the window to an area across Killala Bay and said, "What you are looking for may very well be directly over there."

"Directly over there" meant driving a considerable distance around the boundaries of the bay and through the city of Ballina as well. Several kilometers further north, we found the Killanley Church, the one the B&B proprietor had pointed out from across the bay. As Teresa walked the paths through the cemetery, calling out that she was not having any luck, I kept looking down through the mist at a stone structure that would occasionally show itself. I could see monuments and a Celtic cross, and I began to feel that there was something down there in that foggy valley that we should explore. We got back in the car and drove down into the fog. It was a narrow road, and I had difficulty getting our rented Audi off the road onto a safe parking area. We, of course, encountered an old, rusted-iron gate that required considerable strength to open enough for us to pass; naturally, it screeched at the hinges in objection to being moved.

We explored this forgotten place, with its uneven ground and mounds of grass, until we came upon the remains of a very old chapel and graveyard. Teresa was excited now and searched every stone until I heard a shout through the fog, "Here it is!"

After all of those years, she had found the "Fee" burial ground and tombstones.

After recording the information and taking photographs, we realized that we were damp and chilled, and we decided it was time to leave. We retraced our steps out, and I duly closed the resistant gate. When we got into the car, I turned the ignition key to start the engine. At that moment the word "FEE" appeared on the radio's digital LED read-out in those red capital letters and stayed there for some time — in silence, as the radio had not come on. We both looked at each other, in surprise and shock, and I said, in no uncertain terms, that it was time to go. I started the engine.

The radio came on, and the LED read-out displayed the name of the artist and the song, which it was designed to do. There was no reason on this earth that the word "FEE" should have appeared on that screen.

That eerie, chance occurrence was one of many that Teresa and I experienced in the twenty-five years of researching this book. The story you are about to read is based on pure factual evidence. Though the strange tale I just related is the truth, a solid answer can only be found somewhere beyond the location of that graveyard — I shudder to think where!

Jason P. Goodman M.ED
President and CEO
ALCHEMY STUDIO INC

INTRODUCTION

After 25 years of research for this book, I was finally able to visit the land of my Great Grandmothers and Grandmothers. My husband and I drove the 60 miles from Westport to Belmullet, County Mayo, Ireland, stopping at the lighthouse on Blacksod Bay.

As it was "off season" we were unable to find a charter boat to the island of Inishkea. Near the dock was a pub (naturally). My husband went inside and found a few fishermen enjoying their Guinness. He told them he would "make it worth their while" to take his wife to the island. Exiting the pub a few minutes later, he announced to me that in ½ hour I was to be escorted to my destination.

A young "Skipper" arrived and my husband handed him a "wad" of Euros. I then followed him to his vessel at the dock, a 28ft (8.5m) wood fishing boat, surely a work horse!

The cuddy cabin was just large enough for the

captain and me to stand in. The windows were sea salted, the life vests, looking seldom used, were thrown under the ships wheel. The wheel itself was patched with a bit of duct tape and rope, but we were guided by a sophisticated GARMIN451s with sonar and the skipper's smart phone, well used and sporting a cracked face to match the windows.

I waved to my husband, having complete trust in my new companion. It would prove to be a 40-minute trip to South Inishkea.

It was a beautiful March day without rain, a rarity in Ireland. The island appeared in the west; it was a vision I would later paint on canvas and draw into words — a sky of Cerulean blue, the island a Verde green trimmed with white sand and dotted with light-grey stone cottages, all suspended in the deep blue of the North Atlantic.

I was escorted to the landing pier by dinghy and left on my own while Captain Cawley went off to check his lobster traps with his mate Sean. No one else was on the island; I had the mile of South

Inishkea to explore.

All along the beach were the grey stone homes of the past. Walls and chimneys were still standing, even a few roofs. I had an old map of the homes, so I knew which ones had belonged to the Walsh families. I fail to find words to express this overwhelming experience.

I proceeded to walk to the top of the hill, where I had a view of my Great Grandmother's realm. I envisioned her steps throughout this land — the serenity of the eastern beach, the ferocity of the sea on the western side, and the long stretches of grass where she walked. There were bluffs where I had pictured her waiting for John Padden to arrive in his *currach*. I was standing in the place where I had literally set the scene for this book.

Teresa Marie Fee

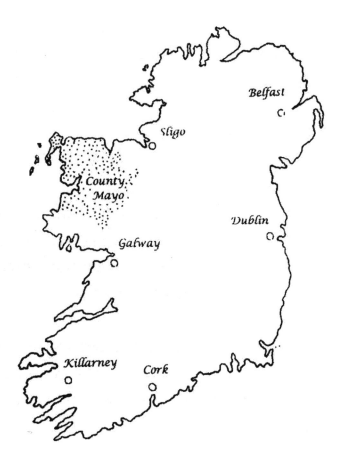

Belfast

C.

Sligo

County
Mayo

Dublin

Galway

Killarney

Cork

PROLOGUE
County Mayo, Ireland

Inishkea Islands, North and South, are situated on the northwest edge of County Mayo, Ireland. They are west of Belmullet, sometimes referred to simply as the "Mullet Peninsula" because of its fish shape. Belmullet is configured north to south, twenty miles long and seven wide and just ½ mile in width at its narrowest point. Following the road south, one comes to Blacksod, where there is the only lighthouse on Blacksod Bay, a guide into this sheltered port, and a reprieve from the unpredictable North Atlantic Ocean.

Over the centuries, many a ship and crew have been lost in this area of the seas. Gale-force winds are common, and the sea is always a threat to the vulnerable.

Approximately three miles west of the Mullet shores are North and South Inishkea. There is a rocky strip of land which connects the two, but a narrow neck of sea water usually covers the spot. It is only when the tide is low and the seas are calm that one can safely walk across. Inishkea South is approximately one mile long and several hundred yards wide. The eastern side, facing the Mullet, has sheltered areas of beach where a vessel could be launched. The western side consists of rocky cliffs 100 to 300 feet high jutting out into the sea. Both islands are dotted with only about twenty homes; all of these are built on the eastern side. The building materials were found there on the island, as stones were plentiful. They were stacked, dry laid, and sealed with lime-mortar made from oyster and clamshells, baked, crushed, and then mixed with the white sand of the island. This sticky substance was also used as a "whitewash" for the exterior of the building. Salvaged wood was used as rafters for the roof and then covered with sod or thatch. The door and any windows faced the leeward side.

Throughout time, the wrecks of many ships on the coast provided much for these island people. Timber from the mangled ships could be used in the houses as doors, mantles, or roof beams. Their furniture could be called "rustic opulence," as the wrecks also provided tables and chairs.

Also found were silver plates, goblets, pitchers, pots, flatware, and even the occasional unbroken dish! Some were very fine porcelain from China.

Over the centuries, there were also a few ships whose demise was not necessarily an accident. It was one dubious way for the islanders to prosper: Signaling a ship during a storm, delivering it onto the rocks, just to get the spoils. The ships at the time were from Spain, France and Scandinavia. Many of the ship's survivors stayed in the area, falling in love with the beautiful Irish women there!

On the rugged ground surrounding the islanders' homes, one would not imagine finding a piano or some gold figurine as a decoration, but it was so. Also, the islanders were known to be able to speak a few languages and play many musical instruments.

Another gift to the islands consisted of fresh-water wells. They were often called "holy wells," as the monks not only used them for the water but lived in the caves surrounding them and incorporated them into their rites. Inishkea and a few of the islands around them were covered with the remains of monks' cells of the "Beehive" type: Built entirely of dry-laid stone, placed one on top of the other until they joined in a peak at the top. They were first supported with a wood frame while being built. When that frame was removed, the weight of the stone kept the cells erect, creating a dome overhead.

The islands were frequented by many migrating birds. Geese of many species and falcons made their nests there. This made for plenty of down, and the beds in the islanders' homes were made very comfortable as a result.

There were sheep and a few cattle to supply milk, cheese and meat. Other provisions for food on the island were the gardens. Stones were stacked to enclose an area for "lazy beds." Trenches were dug, and then sod and dirt were piled in between for the planting area. These were fertilized over the years with seaweed. Of course, the potato was a main crop, but onions, cabbage, and carrots, as well as oats and barley, were grown. The stone walls kept the animals and winds from destroying the garden. But with all of the rest of the island covered in fine green grass, the sheep were allowed to roam wherever they pleased.

The indigo dye from the seashells was a product made on Inishkea. It was a valuable commodity and was sold in the town and to the ships in port. All of the Inishkea women had a jumper of this color and perhaps a wool skirt to match. The women on Inishkea were among the finest weavers in the country, and money was to be made from the blankets they wove.

The men were known as some of the finest fishermen in Ireland. Taking their *currachs* out into the North Atlantic was quite a feat. Some of these vessels could hold ten men. These boats were made by the men themselves. They were lightweight, made of thin wood slats, covered with leather, and then attached to the frame with copper nails. The body of the *currach* was then covered in pitch.

There was another product made for resale, in

the hidden caves of Inishkea: "*Poteen*," a type of Irish liquor known to take your breath away due to its high alcohol content. It was clear and pure and worth its weight in the King's gold, provided you weren't caught in the process of making it! One of the main characters of this story was renowned for the quality and strength of his *Poteen*.

These islanders lived a fine life. They had food from the sea and their gardens, and open spaces of freedom from the rest of the world. They were hardy, healthy, and happy. Because of their isolation, they were spared the wrath of the "Great Famine."

Many stories of the Inishkea islanders have been told. The one you are about to read is factual; it had to be, for it changed the lives of so many involved.

The Walsh family hailed from the southern Island. The head of the house, Padraig, was married to Ellen (Nee) Lavelle, from North Inishkea. He had three daughters and a young son. He was a well-respected man in this small village of twenty families and was considered to be the island's "Master." His ancestors lived on this island for many generations. He was looked upon as a wise and educated man. He was also very knowledgeable about the sea, as he had spent most of his life as a fisherman. He was also a strong man. Physical strength was a must here — only the strong and hardy can survive living on the edge of the Atlantic.

He settled down after falling in love with the fair Ellen Lavelle from the North Island and began raising his own family.

His oldest daughter, Honor, was married and pregnant with his first grandchild.

Kate was his next oldest; she had recently turned sixteen, and Padraig was ready to have her married.

The two youngest children were Rose, thirteen years old, and his only son, Anthony, eleven.
Padraig had arranged Honor's marriage with Sean Keane from North Inishkea. It was a good match

and not difficult, as the two had been sweethearts from a young age.

Padraig was now looking for a suitable husband for Kate. His sights were on a young man from Belmullet: Colm Mahon. Considered wealthy, his father owned the only shop in town. The family lived in a large home on the hill overlooking Binghamstown. He also knew Colm had an eye on his daughter Kate, as she was fair and pretty. This marriage would provide Kate with a comfortable life and a fine home.

This story is about Kate, the young, independent girl, living as a "free spirit" on the island. She has a "mind of her own" and a plan for her future. She is ready for love and will face triumph and tragedy in searching for it.

The year is 1880.

COUNTY MAYO, IRELAND c. 1875

CHAPTER ONE

August 1880

There was to be a horse race on the mainland that day, and all of the Walsh family was to attend. Kate herself owned a pony and thought of herself as a pretty good rider, but this race was for the men only.

The course was on the strand on Elly Bay, Belmullet. Some of the best viewing points were at the top of the dunes, where Kate and Rose secured themselves some seats. They had their father's spyglass, and Kate looked to see which boys would be racing today. Of course, there was Colm Mahon, on his beautiful Connemara horse, one that his "Da" had bought for him. A fine animal he was, and with one of the finest saddles of them all. But there also was her cousin Billy Lavelle and her Uncle Thomas Geraghty among the riders.

She was watching Colm now — especially for how he treated his horse. She had seen him be harsh and unfeeling to his horse and even somewhat brutal to his dogs. He had a dark side to him; she knew that. Even though he was always smiling and the girls always flirting with him because of his good looks, she thought of him as a spoiled boy, not a man.

The shot rang out, and they were off, each rider with a flag of a different color for their fans to cheer on — "Come on RED," for their cousin Billy. His mount was more of a workhorse, but strong and mighty, though maybe not as quick as Colm's. All eight of them were rounding the corner now, a narrow spit of sand, and they were all "clumped" together. With her spyglass, Kate could see Colm push against another rider, making him slip off his saddle, knocking him out of the race. Not fair, but not seen by most. By the time the crowd could see them approaching, there were two horses without a rider at all, just continuing to run along with the others.

Uncle Tom and Billy were close to the head of them all, but Billy's horse was slowing down in the deepest parts of the sand. Staying on the hard, wet sand was ideal, and there was Colm, taking the best of it. "Mr. Mahon comes in first at the finish line," a caller was heard to shout. Cheers went up but not from Kate. Rose thought Colm was a fine man and knew her father would be pleased — just another reason for Kate to marry him.

The crowd moved toward town after the race. There was to be a festival in Binghamstown, and all the townspeople and the islanders who had come across would be there.

All the young girls would be dressed in their best. It was a time to look for a mate, and most of the looking was done by the parents. And Kate knew who her father was seeking in the crowd.

But Kate was quite a beauty now and was aware of the many boys who approached her to talk. She knew that she was pretty and was one of the few girls, women, with blond hair, something she'd inherited from her Viking ancestors. She was also aware that she had grown out of her older sister's hand-me-down clothes. She had filled out her bodice and had to have new clothes made. And she was a bit taller than many of the other girls her age. She couldn't help but flirt, with all the attention she was given. But these were all boys to her — not men. She knew of the man she wanted to be married to, but she hadn't met him as of yet. But that was soon to change.

"Colm, congratulations on the win. There couldn't have been a better horse and rider. Would you come and speak with Ellen and Kate before we head back to the island?"

"Surely, Mr. Walsh. I was wanting to talk to Kate about coming out to see her before you left for England. I was thinking that might be soon."

"Yes, Colm, I'll be leaving in a few weeks with my brothers and some other men from the North Island. I won't be back until before Christmas."

"Hello, Kate. You are looking fine today, as is yourself, Mrs. Walsh. It is so good to see you all in town, especially you, Kate; you don't often come off your island. I've wanted to take you for a ride in my new carriage."

"Well, Colm, I'm quite busy with all the work there is to be done. I myself take care of my own horse, the sheep, and the garden, and I am also every night weaving with the women."

"Oh, Kate! Colm is right. You should come into town more often — whenever your father comes to market."

At that moment, there was a call for the winner of the race to come out of the crowd; Colm was distracted.

"Well, my father will be waiting for me to receive my winnings, so I must be off. I hope to see you soon, Kate."

He tipped his hat to the ladies and walked off; Kate was relieved. There was not a mention of inviting him to dinner. It was getting near sunset, so she knew they would have to set off and get to the island while it was still light. There were at least six other *currachs* leaving at the same time. It was safer to travel together. The weather could change in an instant, and they would look after each other, as all true fishermen do.

Diary: August 30, 1880

What a grand time we had in town today. The fair made a fine end to the summer. I got to have strawberries with ice cream! What a treat! Little Rose was filling herself with chocolate; Da was spending his hard earned money on us for sure today.

I saw some of my friends for the first time in months. The girls from town never come out to Inishkea. "Why should we?" they ask! As if nothing ever happens out on our island. That is fine, —more for me, I say!

Colm was there, and, of course, his horse came in first in the race on the strand. I'd like to knock him off his "high horse" if I could. But Da likes him so, and I am afraid he is getting so close to setting us up to be wed. I saw him talking to Colm's Da, and I could not bring myself to ask what the conversation was about.

But I've got me eye and my heart on the man in the *currach*. I've got to get him to notice me. I think I'm a pretty woman — I saw many of the men and boys looking my way today in town. Now I just need to attract *him*.

CHAPTER TWO

The next day, Kate decided to go visit her Grandmother Lavelle, who lived on the north island. She decided to ride her pony, as it would be quite a distance, and he could wade through the water quite easily. He was dark brown with a creamy colored mane and tail — the color of stout — so her Da had named him "Pint." She brushed him well and threw a heavy wool blanket over his back. She was to deliver the coffee beans father had purchased in town along with some fine brown sugar. Honey was plentiful in the area, but sugar and coffee were treats, something special.

"Oh, Gram, you look so fine in your red skirt, and I see you've been busy at your loom. This is some of the finest wool in Inishkea, and I really like the color you've made this time. We've gathered all of the sage for your red dye this season; now we will have only some of the precious purple to use this winter."

"Have a look in me basket, Kate. I've been saving some of me fine purple wool for Honor's baby blanket. 'Tis only a small amount, so a small wooly blanket will have to do. Oh! And ya have brought me some fine presents. Come — I'll make us a cup of the coffee."

Kate had coffee only at her Gram's house. It was so precious a treat; it was usually tea at home.

"Gram, do you remember when Honor was falling in love with Sean Keane? She came to you to help her have him fall in love with her, and whatever you did must have worked. They are very much in love and are now starting their family. I was wondering if you could do the same for me — I mean, to get a man to fall in love with me, what would I have to do?"

"Oh, 'tis a man you are wanting now. Getting tired of your pony, are ya?"
"

"Oh, Gram, you know I'm more than 16 years old now, and Da is wanting me to get married. So to keep with his wishes, I've come to you."

"Well, there is one way ye can start. Go to the

churchyard at St. Colmcille's, and find a snail on the stone. Put the snail on a tin plate, and cover it with another tin plate. Leave it in the churchyard overnight. In the morning, lift the top plate, and the snail will have written the name of the man ye are goin' to marry."

"But is there a way to make a man love me?"

"Well, you've got to get a snip of his jumper or coat, and bring it to me. I've some special powders to mix with it to make an amulet. Then I'll say me incantations over it. When all that is done, I'll let you wear it next to your breast. His heart will belong to you."

"Till then, I'll be sayin' the devotions and git down on me knees for ya."

"Oh, Gram, I'll be the best granddaughter in the world for ya, to make it work. And I'll be back as soon as I can with the proper piece from his coat."

Kate rode "Pint" back to the south island, this time taking a different route. She rode out to the western cliffs, having to encourage her pony most of the way. It was a windy day, and one could feel the winter coming on. But down on the cliffs, she could see the grey seals; this is why she rode this path. There were a few cubs, barely a day or so old; bundles of white fur, highly desired by wealthy women but not to be touched by Kate. She would not get too close, as their mothers were very protective, and they were large and aggressive "Mums" if their babies were threatened. It was another part of life on the island that Kate loved so. She jumped back up on "Pint," as he was eager to get home to his warm stall.

The "Mullet"

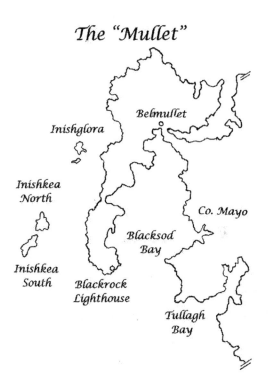

Belmullet

Inishglora

Inishkea
North

Co. Mayo

Blacksod
Bay

Inishkea
South

Blackrock
Lighthouse

Tullagh
Bay

CHAPTER THREE

The sky turned golden, with long, red horizontal streaks, as the sun was setting. The dark silhouette of the island was the only break in the sky; they were almost to Inishkea. Kate and her father were making their way back home with their new purchase — a healthy ram for their flock of sheep. It was late for them to still be out on the rough seas, but the market had been very busy today. Not that Kate minded. It was a thrill to be around the bustle of the marketplace. There were so many more people in town than on the island. She was thankful her father had allowed her to accompany him today.

"Hold on to the horns, Kate. We've just a bit to go now and don't want to lose the new "Da" for my sheep."

With a blindfold and some stabilizing rope, plus the "boots" on his hooves, the big animal was quite secure in the *currach*, one of the largest Da had. The ride was getting a bit too long for his liking, and he was getting restless.

"'Tis a good thing we have been blessed by Saint Deirbhile! Every person who travels upon these waters should do the ritual; all of us Walshes have. Just pass through the east window of the church three times — assuring us we're never to drown."

"Ma will be a bit worried, do you think, Da? But there will be stew and stout waiting for ya. She'll be happy to see us home. I thank you for taking me with you today."

"Well, you are good with the animals, my Kate, and it seemed to me you were in need of an adventure. You've seemed restless lately. Maybe you should go to the mainland more often. Did ya happen to see Colm?"

"Oh, Da, the truth be, I didn't even look for him. Surely there was so much more interesting things to see and do."

"Well, I've wanted to have Colm come out to the house. I'll see him next week when I'm in town. I'm thinking of asking him to come out to speak with your Mum. You know I'll be leaving for the canning season in England. Sure, 'tis not the adventure it used to be when I was a younger man. But it brings us a good wage and keeps us in a stack of turf for the winter."

Many of the men of county Mayo took advantage of the work offered in England in the autumn of the year. It was harvest time, where wheat, barley, oats, as well as potatoes and turnips were so plentiful that it required hiring men from outside the local communities to work the fields. They were paid a good wage — more than an Inishkea man could make fishing. It was worth the few months away from home.

As for the discussion with her Da about Colm, this was not the first time the subject had come up. Kate was not pleased that her father was arranging her marriage. Colm Mahon had been his choice for her. Colm's father was the owner of the town's only linen mill, and Colm, as the only son, would inherit the lot. But he had lived in town all his life. He would never move to the island, and she wanted to stay there. She had such a full life on Inishkea. She loved it and was not keen to leave or to be wed to Colm Mahon! She had another man in her sights. But this was not the time to tell Da.

Up onto the shore they were. While Da took hold of the ram, Kate tied the *currach*. She grabbed the small bundle of gifts for the family and headed toward the cottage.

"Kate, go on and tell your Ma we are safe at home, God be thanked. I'll get to the fields to let this man run about. I'll be in for my supper soon." Kate hurried off toward the lights shining from the windows of their cottage. It would be warm in there, and there would be some stew waiting. She had bought a gift for her sister Honor, who was pregnant with her first child. Tomorrow, she would ride over to her place and visit, and give her the bundle.

But she also had plans for the early morning, as, on Sunday, *he* would be coming to the island. She planned to be up and out early with the sunrise and be there at the shore when he arrived. She would talk to him tomorrow. It was time. Also, she would bring her Mum's small scissors to get that piece of cloth for the amulet.

"Oh, girl, where have you and your Da been? I've been stirring this pot for hours. And all the time praying ye weren't part of the sea. Give me your wet shawl, and take off those old boots of yours."

Kate's mother, Ellen, was untying the laces now, in a hurry. "Oh, Kate, I wish you had come back with a new pair of boots. These will never make it through the winter. What were ye both doing in town for such a long time?"

The door blew open, and Padraig stomped in, followed by a gust of wind and rain.

"Glory be, Da, if you don't look a fright, and the jumper wet and dirty from that new "man" ye brought back! Ah, sit, and have your supper; I'll pour the stout."

"Ah, Ma, it was a great day. The town was black with people. Couldn't stop sayin' "Hello" to 'em all. And they were all asking about you, Ma: 'Why doesn't Ellen come into town more often? We miss her.'"

"Well, I prefer to stay on me island. I don't care much for the crowds like I did when I was going to the dances and keeping me eye on you, Padraig! When I was Kate's age, I was going to the mainland to look for fun and me future husband!

"So, Kate — did ya see and talk to Colm? He is such a fine young man. And going to be wealthy someday, I'd say. He'll provide a good home for you — a life of leisure, I'd be thinking."

Was this the time to tell them? Finishing a bite of bread, she was preparing to tell them of the man in the boat. But how could she? She didn't even know his name. It would have to wait. She'd have to get to know him first.

Diary: September 6, 1880

Today was a great day. Da and I went to Belmullet to the market. We bought a huge ram for the
herd. 'Twas fun to see all the girls my age, showing off their fine skirts and shawls and flirting with
the boys, all too young for me. I may not have the
fancy dresses, but I make a better wife than all of
them. None of them could ride a pony like me.
None of them could handle the sheep like I can.
And Mum has taught me to cook! They all seem
so weak to me. I'd rather be strong. I know I could
take care of myself. I saw Da talking to Colm, but I
hid myself, as I have no desire to talk to him.

Tonight, Da talked about him coming to court me.
I wanted to tell him "No," but I also don't want to
make Da cross. Someday soon, I'll tell him about
that man in the boat. I hope to meet him soon.
Please let him fall in love with me. Please, God!

CHAPTER FOUR

Soon the island would be left without any men on it, as they would all be going to work the harvest. During that time, the women were to be left alone, and most all men from the mainland or anywhere else were not allowed to visit. Every home was equipped with a firearm of some kind as protection. It was a big adventure for the younger men. Getting to see the world, they said. Sometimes, some of them did not return — finding work, adventure, or even a wife to keep them away. But Da would be back. And he always came back with some very special gifts.

"I'll be off tomorrow, over the seas to England, to work. To make enough money for the taxes, the turf, and the special things I'd like my family to have. There will be some fine gifts this Christmas, for sure!"

"I've put in enough turf to last a few weeks, and I've patched the roof, to keep ye all dry! Ma, if there is anything you need, all ye have to do is see John Padden. He'll be stopping to see my own Ma to get what she may need — anything I may have forgotten. He will be coming by here on Sunday next, so, if you need anything, wait for him at the landing. I'll pay him when I return. John will be bringing some turf for both you and my Ma."

So, now I do know his name, Kate thought.

"Da, is it he, John Padden, the only man we will allow to come onto the island while you are away? We aren't to shoot him, then? Ha! Most of the Belmullet men know not to come here while our men are away. They know to fear the women here on Inishkea. We must protect ourselves, don't you think?"

"Girl, don't shoot the man who might be feeding ya! Try not to kill any person while your Da is not here. I don't want to be goin' to a hanging! Sure you're my own Grace O'Malley!"

"Ah, Da, ya know I'll be good."

Padraig and the whole family were up before dawn the next day. All of the men were gathered with their families at the boat launch for a send-off. Some of the little ones were laughing and playing. Of course, they didn't understand that they wouldn't be seeing their fathers again for a few months. Maybe that was harder on the fathers, as it would be a long time not being able to see their young ones. The men would be taking some of the largest *currachs* to Belmullet. There were *currachs* of many sizes, and some were small enough for one person to handle. These were left for the women, should something arise to make it necessary to make a trip to the mainland.

Hugs and kisses, and off they went into the sunrise. Afterwards, many of the women had tea at the Walshes' home. Plans were made for the evening weaving sessions and the days they would be together for some card playing or music. They were all quite good friends, if not cousins! They also knew that, if there were any troubles, they were all armed — a rifle in every cottage — just in case.

Although it was a sad day when the men left, the first few days brought a sense of freedom, as the women could make their own schedules, not having the man to cook for. But, after that, the days got lonely. It was best to keep busy.

And that they did.

Diary: September 10, 1880

Da, Sean, and most of the men left for the autumn harvest. Poor Anthony wanted to go, but he will have to wait a few more years: He is still too young. But we told him that he is the man of the island now! He will be the man to protect all of us Inishkea women!

The following Sunday, Kate was up early. The sun was rising and entered her window, casting soft light across her face. She preferred to wake this way. Next, she could hear the chickens and the old rooster calling out to the world. Funny old guy — he thinking this is his island!

She fluffed up the feather mattress and shook out the quilt. Then she picked out her best skirt, bodice, and jumper to wear. It was Sunday, but she was not dressing for that particular occasion. She hoped to see *him* today. After sunrise he could usually be seen rowing his way toward the island. She would be there to greet him this time. And she was going to look her best. She'd make him notice.

She set a pot of fresh water over the fire for her bathing. She kept heating water until the copper tub was quite full. She washed her long blond hair and bathed her body with the special bar of soap she'd purchased on the mainland (she had kept this a secret!). She used a sachet of crushed heather and rubbed herself with it. Looking at her naked self in the "great" mirror, she was pleased. She felt even more like a woman now. As her hands moved slowly across her body, she felt desires as well. She wanted to know a man. And not just any man, but the one she had been watching for months now — the man in the *currach*, the handsome one coming today.

"Are ya not ready for church then, Kate?" her mother asked. "I'm leaving now with Rose and Anthony; we're going to stop at Gram's. We'll meet you at the church." Kate dressed; she even put on her shoes! She grabbed her best shawl and borrowed one of her Ma's. She headed down to the southern tip of Inishkea. There she would keep an eye on the east, watching for him. Today, she would talk to him. Today he would see her. She felt confident this time, not afraid. Today, he would know her name.

It was a cool day, and the wind was blowing a bit. So she found herself an area to sit in that was protected from the western wind but had a good view of Blacksod Bay and any vessel that would be on it. She could see a dark spot, south of the lighthouse, but it was too far away to know for sure.

I should have brought Da's glass, Kate thought, *as then I would know for sure if it was him. But should I lose or break that, it would be the death of me! If it is him, I shall know in an hour. That's when he will be in full view, close enough to see.*

CHAPTER FIVE

It was him; she could see the movement of his shoulders and muscular back, rowing toward her. She was nervous and excited, forgetting the words she had so carefully rehearsed. But she remained confident. Today, he would be met by Kate only, and he would know her for certain. She ran her fingers through her long blond hair, pinched her cheeks, and ran her tongue across her moist lips.

As he rowed to the shore, she walked down to the area of the dock where a stone wall was stacked with lobster traps and ropes. He didn't notice her at first, as he was busy pulling the *currach* up onto the sand to keep it stable, as it was piled high with turf.

She was standing where she could not be missed; she had thrown off a few of the many shawls she had on to keep warm. As he turned toward her, a sudden gust of wind lifted her long, golden locks in all directions, like the rays of the sun.

"Ha!" he laughed!

Kate was immediately angry — her "Irish" came up like the gust of wind! This was not the romantic meeting she had imagined.

"What do you want here? Don't you know no man is allowed on Inishkea until Christmas?"

"Calm yourself, girl. Don't chase me away just yet. I didn't mean to anger you so. It's just that I'd never before seen the sun rising in the west. Your beautiful hair is what I was meaning."

"Oh, so, now, you are trying to charm me into letting you stay."

"I've only come to deliver something. I was told to give it to the pretty daughter of Padraig Walsh, by the name of Kate. I'm now guessing that mighten' be you."

"And who is it you've been talking to, then?"

"Well, I've been asked by Colm Mahon to deliver something to you."

As he looked through items in his *currach*, Kate smoothed her hair. *He thinks I'm pretty*, she thought — and blushed.

"Here it is, delivered safe and sound. 'Tis this box."

"That wee thing?"

"Yes, I was told you could open it now, unless you've the patience to wait until Christmas, which is some weeks off."

"I've really no interest in it a'tall. I've no interest in the boy Colm Mahon."

"Well, I was thinking it was something special. Maybe it be you and he are getting married?"

"Certainly not, sir. I'll be the one who makes the decision of who my husband will be, and I'm not interested in that boy."

He was staring into her now — *right through me,* she thought. She was beginning to feel uncomfortable. He was quite handsome. His face was weathered by the sun and wind, and she could not tell his age. But he was rugged and strong, and had a nice smile. She was no longer angry that he had laughed. Now, she felt pleased.

"My father has something to do with this gift; I wouldn't want to open it unless he was present. And he won't be back for some time. I think you should keep that box until he returns."

"I would not want to be the one responsible for losing this — wouldn't want it to fall out of the boat and end up in the sea. Perhaps you could give it to your Grand mum to hold for you?"

"Oh, my good sir, a much better idea would be to have that box hidden somewhere. One of the holy wells would have a place for it. It can be held there until my Da returns."

"Surely it will be a bit tempting to have something this mysterious somewhere within your reach for so many days. Are you not curious as to its contents, then?"

"No, you can hide it where you wish. I've no interest in the box — or in the boy who sent it."

He was staring at her quite intensely now. She was excited and did not know what to say. Was he interested in her? It *seemed* so.

"Well, I'll go off and put it somewhere safe, then. Will you still be here when I return?"

"Surely, as it seems I am the only woman keeping watch on the island today. I had better keep everyone safe from you. I'll be waiting for your return."

She watched as he walked toward the high cliffs on the western side of the island. There would be many hiding places along the coast. It was where Da's still of *poteen* was hidden; even she did not know its whereabouts. She hoped John Padden would not find it.

The small scissors in her pocket reminded her of the amulet Gram was to make. There was an old jumper lying in his *currach*, so she went for a snippet of it.

She was doing a bit of daydreaming now. *John Padden, what a man you are. Handsome, strong — and I'll bet you are a good kisser! I've been wanting to be kissed — by a man, not one of those stupid boys in town. Really kissed — I'm ready!*

He surprised her by returning from a different direction, coming from behind her.

"Oh, sir — you startled me."

"No need to be afraid of me Kate. I'll do you no harm."

"I know nothing about you, Mr. Padden."

"'John' is the name."

"Well, John, you tell me you have been coming to the island for a long time. Do you know my Grandmother, then?"

"Sure, Kate, I know *both* of your Grandmothers:

Lavelle and Walsh. I've been delivering turf to them for a few years. You must have been too busy growing up to notice me."

"Well, I'm grown up now, as you can see."

"Yes, I can see that, fair Kate. You must be of marrying age if you are getting gifts brought to you across the bay."

"Well, I am of age to be in love, and I haven't decided who that might be."

"Ha! *You* have not decided. I think your Da might be the one to be doing that for ya."

"No, I'll be the one to decide who I shall love and marry.

"And what of you, John Padden — who has your heart?"

"Me? No, not I. I've no woman in my life. I work too much, and I be gone from home too long for a woman to want to be my wife. I guess you could say I be married to the sea."

"But it must be so lonely for you. Would you not want a woman to be there when you get home?"

"Sure, it would be nice, but I am a loner. Even my family has gone. I live alone in the Bay — just me and me goats."

"I am a loner as well, John. It is just me and my pony — that is all I care about. I also want to know love. But I shall not love a boy. I must have a *man* to love me."

"Well you certainly are pretty enough to have any man love you. Sure, it would not be an old sea-man such as myself that would make you happy."

"And what makes you think that? Why would I not love a strong, handsome man such as yourself?"

"Oh, you are a bit of a flirt, girl. But 'tis good for a young woman to know her own mind — not have someone else making all the decisions for you. You are a bit of a strong one, yourself."

In the distance, church bells could be heard.

"Why are you not in church, my darlin'?"

"I don't always go; I have some questions about religion. I don't understand why so many die for it."

"You are right there, girl, and 'tis surely the root of many of the troubles here in Ireland. I myself have lived without God — as far as God ever lets a man live without *Him*. God to me is out there on the sea and in the sky; *that* is my church.

"Ah, I must be going now, Kate. I hear the bells, and the time be passing too fast. I've got to get back to my deliveries."

"Will you be coming back very soon, John?"

"Would ya like for me to return, Kate?"

"Yes, yes. I'm thinking we have more talking to do between us."

"Talking? Surely, I will be back to see you — even though a man is to be shot for stepping his foot on this island while the men are away. But it would be worth it — that it would."

Her heart leapt. "So, I shall see you again soon? Is it just on Sunday that you come this way?"

"Well, I could make it back here this Thursday coming, if it would please ya."

"Oh, it would, John. I would like that very much, indeed."

"Then I shall see you Thursday, about the same time. Now take care of your pretty self, and don't go breaking a leg looking for that box."

"Ha! Now 'tis *me* that has to laugh. I've no interest in it a'tall. My interest is in someone else at this moment."

CHAPTER SIX

That evening, Kate decided to visit her pregnant sister, Honor. She had brought back something from the mainland and wanted to deliver it, as she knew her sister had been working on a dressing gown for her child's baptism.

She threw a heavy wool blanket over "Pint," her pony. She wore an old pair of Da's trousers, as this is what she preferred when she rode.

She could see the light in the window of the cottage in the distance. She hadn't been to visit her sister for a week or more now, and she was feeling a touch guilty. Kate had promised to come by often to help with the chores since Honor's husband, Sean, had gone off with the other men to England.

"Hello, Honor — 'tis me, Kate. Shall I come in?"

"Oh, yes, Kate. The door's not locked. Come in. Oh, 'tis so good to see ya. I've been holding back on fetching water, hoping ya would be coming by.

I'm getting so big now, it makes me laugh, but I'm a bit afraid to carry anything too heavy, such as the likes of that water pail."

"Oh, Honor, 'tis my fault. I'll fill the cistern to the brim while I'm here, dear sister. I've brought you the fabrics and lace that Mum bought for you at market. I know you've been hoping to finish the gown for the baby, and the things are beautiful. You'll be pleased."

"Oh, Kate, 'tis lovely bits of lace, just enough for the trim on the color and cuff. And tiny bits of silk ribbon! Oh, I'll find a place for these as well. Thank you and Mum; it will be a lovely gown when it's finished.

"It is what has been keeping me busy, passing the time, missing Sean so."

"Must be hard, then, to have the man you love disappear for so long, Honor. Tell me what it is like to be in love. How does it make you feel?"

"Oh, it can make your heart flutter, like a butterfly in your chest. It can make it jump, like you've been tickled in surprise. Or it can feel like a heavy stone on your breast. It makes the heart go mad! That is what I think love does to a heart. Someday, you will know, and, from what I hear from Mum, that will not be long, as Da is arranging a meeting with Colm Mahon for you."

"Honor, I've no interest in that boy, and I've told Mum. But I'm almost afraid to tell Da. He is so determined to get us together. But I've got my eye and a bit of my heart set on someone else. Someone who makes my heart do the things you just spoke of — all the fluttering and thrills."

"And who is this mysterious boy, then?"

"It is not a boy, but a man. And I'm thinking he feels something for me."

"Well, this is a bit of news and a mystery. Do I know this man?"

"You may have seen him at Gram's cottage. He often delivers the turf from the mainland to her."

"Not the tall, dark-haired man from Tullagh Bay? I think his name is Padden."

"Yes, that would be him, Honor. He has captured my heart!"

"Oh, Kate, you cannot be serious. He is too old for ya, and he has the "falling sickness,"[1] which ya might catch. That is why he has no woman."

"But Honor, I've no attraction to any of the boys Da has had in mind for me. *He* is a man, and not too old. He just has the weathered skin of a sea-man. And I am not a girl! I feel like a woman. He makes me feel like one."

"I don't know what you mean by that Kate, but you know Da and Mum will not approve.

"Colm is wealthy and good looking, and, yes, I would call him a man as well."

"I cannot stop the feelings I already have. I think I am in love. Just as you described it is how I feel about him."

1 Epilepsy

"Oh, sister, you've gotten yourself in a terrible place. I think you had better stop this foolish thinking you have for him. Colm Mahon is much better suited for you."

Kate slowly lowered her head as she felt her eyes fill. But she knew she must not cry.

"I was hoping *you* would understand, Honor. I've only you I can talk to and say what I truly feel. Remember how you talked about Sean before you were married? We used to sit up late in our beds and talk. You told me so much then that, now, I was thinking I could talk to you, and you would understand. I need you to stand by me, Honor, when I tell Da and Mum about John Padden."

"And you've been seeing this John, have you?
"
"Yes, he often comes to the island. I know he loves me. I can just tell it is so."

"Has he asked to talk to Da?"

"No. He knows Da will not be back until after the

harvest. I'm sure he will."

"I don't know what to say to you, Kate. I, of course, want you to be happy and have love in your life. But I just don't know if you're choosing the right man, 'tis all."

They sat together for a bit longer, and Honor's attention was directed back to the dressing gown she was sewing.

"I'll tend to the water now before it gets dark outside. Then I should be getting back home."

Kate was angry and hurt, but she dared not show it. She didn't want to upset her sister. So she decided she would just carry on without anyone's approval.

As they said their goodbyes, Kate could see the look of concern on Honor's face. But Kate was done talking and turned away, promising to return soon.

Diary: October 6, 1880

It was no use talking to Honor; she didn't believe I could be in love with John Padden. She must have forgotten all the support I gave to her when she was wishing for the affection of Sean Keane. To-morrow, I will see John. Maybe I can get him to tell me of his plans for us — and tell me of his home on Tullagh Bay. He must have a fine cottage.

CHAPTER SEVEN

Kate was at the dock early the next day, waiting. She could see the boat in the distance, coming toward Inishkea; it would be him. Today, she wanted something to happen. She wanted to feel like a step toward their future together would be taken.

He pulled the *currach* up onto the sand and secured it to a landing post. As he turned around, Kate jumped into his arms. They laughed as he steadied them, and he spun her around and around. And then they stopped and kissed. It was their first kiss — at first playful, and then more passionate.

"I've been waiting for you to kiss me like that, John. I just cannot wait any longer to be held in your arms."

"Well, then you should be interested to know that I have packed us a basket of food. I also have a small bottle of *poteen*, which I had planned to share with you on Duvillaun Mor Island. Would you like to be getting away from Inishkea with me for a time?"

"I'd be thrilled, John! Quick — let us be off!"

Kate climbed into the boat, and John gave them a good shove off toward the island just south of Inishkea. It would take about a half hour of good rowing to get there. Kate knew her Mum would be at Gram's tonight, doing the weaving, so she had not to worry about the time. And she covered her head with her shawl, in the event some other eyes from the island were watching.

"Did you know that the monks and the nuns would use the Holy Wells as a meeting place? You see, they were all young, and they would meet at the wells for pleasurable reasons. There was no rule someone had to be celibate so many years ago. The wells were known as 'trysting' places."

Kate had heard the word "tryst" once before. To her knowledge, it meant "to play."

Duvillaun Mor was a deserted island, except for the few grey seals and the many birds. There were the remains of a few of the monks' cells there. Some even had a roof that was intact after hundreds of years.

John found a cell, with a moss floor and the door facing the east, out of the Atlantic breeze. He carried the basket of food and drink and a few blankets into the shelter.

"Come, dear Kate. I've a 'nest' all made up for us."

"Ha! And a lovely one it is, Mr. Padden, but I think you could do with some lime wash on the walls!"

"Come, sit here. The moss is soft, and I'm surprised how dry 'tis in here. I used to come here as a boy. I'd spend many a night here if my Da was in the mood for beating me."

"Oh, John. I didn't know that. You've never said a thing about your family. Only that they've all gone."

"Years ago, my Mum died, and my Da was always drinking the *poteen*. My sister left first — to

America, I think. But my father had a brother in Dingle, so he left me. I guess I was about fifteen years old at the time. I was glad to be rid of him. I haven't heard a thing from anyone since."

Kate moved closer to him and took his hand in hers. As he stared out over the bay, she studied him — his hands, his profile. She loved him and felt his pain.

He turned to her and took her face in his hands. They kissed — at first, lightly, but then deeply, passionately. She could taste him, sweet and salty. Their breathing became deeper and heavier; they moved their bodies to be next to each other. John gently laid her down on the blanket.

"You are such a desirable woman, Kate Walsh. I don't want to hurt you; you may stop me if you wish."

"Yes, yes, John — I do want this. I want to know you. I want to lay with you. I want us to make love, to be in love."

She pulled her jumper off over her head. Many of the buttons on her blouse were open, as she had done that earlier. She knew he could see her breast under her bodice. She brought his hand around to the front and had him untie the bow. She unbuttoned the waist of her skirt. He took off his jacket and jumper; and his chest was bare. His body felt warm as he pulled her to him.

Their hands were exploring now, touching each other's bodies. She felt between his legs and, at first, was startled, but willing. He pulled off her skirt, and they both lay naked. She wanted to tell him how she loved him, but his mouth covered hers in passion. She reached down to him and felt what was soon to be inside her. He gently spread her legs. Though tense, she gave in and felt his weight upon her.

A moan slipped from her lips, and she gripped his back as they gave themselves to each other. *Giving and taking — that is what one does in love,* Kate thought. That was what she was experiencing now: true love. He wanted her and she him. They were united as one: they belonged to each other.

CHAPTER EIGHT

"Where have you been, girl? Tonight you were to be helping with the weaving at your Grandmother's. And would you look at that skirt? It is one of your best — 'tis all wet and dirty. What have you been up to?"

"Oh, Mum, it was the new ram! I couldn't find him, so I walked forever, looking; you know how precious he is to Da! I finally found him stranded on some rocks below the cliffs. I had to wade out into the water. He was a stubborn one, and I was a bit afraid of him, with his size and all. I managed to get him to cross over to the sand, but, by then, he had me all wet and dirty."

"Well, give me your skirt, then, and I'll hang it by the fire. And you'd better go and wash yourself a bit before you sit down for some tea."

"I'm not hungry, Mum. I am too tired. I think I'll wash a bit and get into my bed, if you don't mind."
"Oh, go on with yourself. Surely I'll be glad when your little brother Anthony is big enough to do

your Da's chores. You have always been a bit too adventurous to my way of thinking. Too much like your Da, I suppose."

Diary: October 7, 1880

LOVE: That is what I found today! And I know now that I am a woman. Yes — today I became a woman! I love John Padden, and he loves me — I just know it. I am so tired, but now I know what it is like to be loved. It can be exhausting, but oh, so beautiful.

Mum doesn't know. I suppose I spun a good yarn. Hope God is forgiving that. And I hope I'm forgiven for what John and I did today. But I feel blessed, as we have the love for each other. I can't wait to see him again. Goodnight my dearest, goodnight.

The following days were stormy. There was no going out for walks, unless one had to! All the sheep were inside their shelter, and so was "Pint." Even the pony was not up for leaving. There would be no one arriving at the landing, so no reason to sit out in the storm waiting and watching. Kate kept herself busy helping Mum with "putting up" some berries for jam and doing the knitting. All of the men would need new jumpers when they returned. Their old ones would be getting dirty and torn from working. Kate remembered she had taken a few threads from the jacket that John had on that day on Duvillaun Mor. She decided it was time to get them to Gram.

"I was thinking of going over to Gram's tonight Mum. Shall I bring a jar of the jam?"

"And why would you be wanting to go out in this weather, Kate? Are ya a bit mad?"

"Oh, Mum, 'tis just a short distance, and I worry that Gram will be lonely. I won't be away for long. I'll take 'Pint' if you think it would be better."

"No, that pony of yours will run off or throw ya into the sea. Leave him in; cover yourself to keep dry."

It was a wet and windy evening, but Kate was de-termined to get to her Gram's cottage. The land bridge was barely visible, and her old boots got wet to the ankle crossing it.

"Gram, 'tis me, Kate. Can you let me in?"

"Oh, my sweet girl, come in, come in. What are ya doing out on a night like this? Oh, ya brought me some of Ellen's jam; lovely!"

"Gram, do you remember how you said you could help me have a man be in love with me? Well, I've got a bit of the fabric you need for the charm I'm to wear."

"And what did the snail write for ye?"

"I couldn't read a thing, Gram; I don't think that snail knew how to spell!"

"Well, give me the pieces, and I'll make the amulet for ya. I've a bit of linen from me own wedding dress that I'll use for the sack. Give me the man's article; that will go inside with some crushed rose quartz, rosemary, heather, and clover. Ye are to wear this when you are with him, and he will be smitten by Kate Walsh. Wear this amulet on your bosom, next to your heart. I'm sure it will make him fall in love with you. It has worked for every woman who ever came to me."

"Gram, I hope to be just like you when I'm old — wise and helpful to all!"

"Now, go on home girl. I don't like the sound of that wind out there. Unless ya want to stay with your old Gram tonight?"

"Mum would be worried for sure, Gram, so off I go with me new amulet of love!"

CHAPTER NINE

Kate rode "Pint" over to see her sister Honor. She needed to talk to someone about what was happening to her relationship with John. Two months had gone by without her seeing him. She wanted so much to just take a *currach* and go and find him. She knew he lived in Tullagh Bay — but not which cottage. But she was stuck on the island; none of the women would trust themselves with taking a boat to the mainland.

She was surprised to see the size of her sister! "Heavy with pregnancy," as they say. Kate and Honor had a fine pot of tea together, and then Kate helped her sister get the house ready for Sean's return. Also, she wanted to decorate a bit for Christmas. Kate tied some red ribbons on the curtains and put some greens about the room. Her sister had made candles from sheep fat and added cinnamon: They smelled delicious!

When they finally sat down again, she told Honor she needed her help.

"Honor, how did you know when you were pregnant?"

"Kate, a woman just *knows*. Her body tells her; it is like a glow inside. Ye may look the same on the outside, but, inside your body, there is a voice that tells ya; 'tis quite wonderful!"

"Don't ya be worried about me now, little sister, I know I'm as big as a whale, but I feel fine, and I'm strong — you know that. Living out here on this Island, you just have to be. And if I can't make it into town to have this baby, I'll be fine. Barbara Keane is right next door, and our Aunt Biddy is willing to come from Belmullet and stay if need be."

"I'm just so happy right now — my life is so good. Sure 'twill be perfect soon, as soon as Sean comes through that door."

She couldn't do it. Kate could not spoil her sister's joy by telling her that she might — yes, she probably was — pregnant. She was getting scared. Where was John? Where was John Padden?

Diary: December 10, 1880

Da is home, as well as Sean and my cousins. They all look like they need a few good meals put into them, but they are beaming with joy to be back. And so are we, and I've never seen Honor so happy. Tomorrow, she will be taken to Belmullet to the hospital to have the baby. It is her first, and Barbara Keane thinks she should have a doctor with her. I've asked Da and Sean if I can go along, and they were happy to have another woman with them. So, I shall be in town. I'm hoping to find John. If I cannot, I've written a letter that I hope somehow to get to him. He must be told, he must know: I'm pregnant with his child. Not that anyone could tell from looking at me, but, just like Honor said, I *know*. My body has told me so, and I have not had any bleeding since before Duvillaun Mor. Please, God, let me see John tomorrow.

CHAPTER TEN

It was a bit of a rough ride to the mainland, and poor Honor was the color green when we got there. Aunt Bridget — "Biddy" — was there with her pony cart to take them the rest of the way. Da and Uncle Thomas stopped in town at their favorite pub while Sean and Kate went along to the hospital. All along the way, Kate was keeping her eyes open for him, whether out on the bay or walking in town. John lived too far from town to be there on horse — if he had a horse. Kate didn't know if he did.

"How are you, Kate?' asked Aunt Bridget. "I haven't seen you in ages. My own God-daughter, and you never come to see me. The last time was when Maureen and Francis were leaving for Sligo and then on to a ship for America. That was eight months ago now. It was not easy saying goodbye to my only daughter. But there was nothing here for Francis, no work to support them. Maureen was scared, but ye must do what your husband thinks is right to keep the family together. I've had a few letters from her; she finds living in America hard and misses us terrible. I'm so happy I'll have my nieces here and now one with a baby!"

Once at the hospital, they helped Honor inside, where they waited for the doctor to see her.

"Aunt Biddy, do you think I can take a few minutes to run down to town? I've not seen my girlfriends for some time now."

"Go ahead, young lady, and, when you are ready, we'll meet at the cart. I know your Da will want to be getting back to Inishkea before sunset. I'll stay here with Honor and Sean."

Kate quickly headed down the hill. She knew where her Da and Uncle would be, so she stayed away from that part of town; it was best she not run into them. She looked down at the harbor to see if *his* boat was there. Many of them looked alike, but she would recognize John's — it always had a dusting of "turf" on the bottom. She saw the small boat belonging to Colm. It was just big enough for one person to handle.

She certainly did not want to run into *that* boy. She threw her shawl around her head, hoping to cover her blond tresses.

She walked into the market area: No John. She looked into the windows of pubs: No John. She decided to take the letter to the post office — maybe there would be an address for him. As she turned the corner, there was Colm.

"Kate, what are you doing here? It is so good to see you. What did you think of my gift? Have you told your Da? I was thinking of coming out to Inishkea on Saturday. It's time we arranged our marriage. I'm so looking forward to it, Kate. You're looking a wee bit scared. Are you OK?"

"Yes, Colm, but I can't talk to you now. My sister is having her baby, and I've got to get to the hospital, right now!"

"Oh, I'll run up there with you. Maybe I can get us a carriage — would that help?"

"No, 'tis better I am alone. Honor is shy and

wouldn't want me bringing any men into the hospital room. I had better go. I'll be seeing you soon, Colm. Goodbye!"

Now she was *really* confused. What could she do? She just *had* to find John. She walked quickly up toward the hospital and then turned around to see if Colm was behind her. She could see him heading the other way, toward town.

She got an idea: She would take Colm's boat! She would make for Tullagh Bay. She knew to head south, toward the Blacksod Lighthouse. When that was directly to her West, she would turn toward the East and John's home. She decided that was her only option. No one noticed as she rowed out past the bigger fishing boats in the harbor. She would keep close to the mainland shore. It would not be easy and might take an hour, but she was determined. Colm could right now be talking to her Da. He could be asking for the marriage to take place as soon as possible.

Back at the hospital, the doctor said Honor was ready, right then! She barely had time to believe it when she went into labor. Sean and Aunt Biddy were there with her, holding her hands. Sean was telling her how much he loved her. Aunt Biddy was telling her how to breathe. Honor, writhing in pain and crying with joy, was having her baby!

CHAPTER ELEVEN

It was close to an hour before Kate reached Tullagh Bay. To the West was the lighthouse. She turned the opposite way, rowing into the boggy bay. She remembered John telling her about how he had to watch the tides closely, as the water level had to be just right for him not to get stuck in the mud near his home. There were a few cottages next to each other, but she could see another one off by itself. *That may be John's — the loner,* she thought.

She saw his *currach* and pulled next to it. She tied the boat and ran toward the house. She knocked and then opened the door. There was John, on the floor, trembling and shaking — the "falling sickness!" She put her arms around him, and he settled. She could see a bit of blood on the side of his mouth. She was frightened.

Slowly, he opened his eyes; he seemed not to recognize her or his whereabouts.

"John, it is me, Kate! I've come to you. You have to

want me. I know you need me. Where have you been all these weeks? Why have you not come for me?"

He released himself from her arms and rose up and sat in a chair.

"No, Kate, no. You should not have come here."

"But you need me, John, and I need you. You showed me you loved me, and then you disappeared. I was afraid, so I came to you."

"No, Kate, we cannot be. You see how I am. I have this illness, and you cannot cure me of that — no one can. And you cannot live with a man like me. No."

"But, John, we are in love, and I must tell you also that I'm going to have your baby."

He dropped his head in his hands, and Kate could tell he was crying.

"John, we can be happy. I can give you children,

and you will never again be alone. We can get married now."

"It is wrong, Kate. I knew it was wrong, but I desired you so, you made it so hard to stay away. But we should not have carried on like we did. You cannot give your life to a sick man like me."

"I don't care about your sickness, John; I care about you — and our child."

"A child! Oh, dear God, what have I done? What have I done to you, girl?"

"You've made me happy, John — that's what you've done. And I will do the same for you. We can run away together if we must, or I can stay here with you, forever."

In town, the news of a baby boy reached Da and Uncle Thomas. They were headed toward the hospital when they ran into Colm. "Mr. Walsh, I've just been told that Kate has taken my boat out of the harbor. Why do you think she would do such a thing?"

"My Kate, taking a boat? What kind of nonsense are you talking, Colm? Look, now, we are in a big hurry. My daughter Honor just had a baby, and I've got to get to the hospital."

"But, Mr. Walsh, what shall I do about Kate and my boat?"

"Colm, if what you say is true — and I doubt it — come back to the hospital. I've got to go, and Thomas is running ahead of me. I'm going now!"

At the hospital, all were crying and laughing at the sight of this little newborn.

"Oh, Honor, you've given us a fine boy — fine, indeed!"

"Sean, you are a Da now. How do you feel?"
"I'm so proud — proud of you, my dear wife, and proud to have a son."

"Padraig, ye are now a Grandfather!"

"Grand, simply grand!"

"We shall name him Padraig, like his Grandpa! He is to be our 'Paddy.'"

CHAPTER TWELVE

"Kate, this cannot be. I've got to take you back to Inishkea, right now."

"But, no, John! I want to stay here with you. Don't you want to be my husband? I'll make a good wife — you'll see. I can cook and am good with the animals; I can sew and weave; 'tis nothing I cannot do for a man."

John wiped the blood from the corner of his mouth and began to put on his heavy coat.

"See this, Kate? I've once again bitten my tongue. I won't have a woman watching me writhing around the floor — I will not have it! I have been alone too long to have a woman in my life. How can I be a father? No — it will not be."

He walked out the door, leaving Kate behind. He tied the small boat to his *currach* and called for her to come.

"I'll not have you stay here, Kate. Come, now. I

shall get you back to where you belong, back on Inishkea."

Crying, Kate put on her wrap and shawls and walked to the boats. She had lost all control of her life. What was she to do? First her Da had a plan for her. Then she thought she saw her future in John Padden. She fell in love. She was a woman in love, and now he was pushing her away. And what of the baby she was carrying? What was to be their future?

"Where did ya get this little boat, Kate?"

"I took it from the Belmullet harbor. I was there because my sister is in the hospital; she is going to have her baby."

"Well, truth be told, you are a brave one, Kate."

Colm was waiting outside the hospital when Padraig came out.

"It is true, Mr. Walsh. She was seen heading south along the shore; some fishermen saw her. Where would she be going at this hour — and in my *boat*? Do you think she would be on her way to see John Padden?"

"John Padden? What has he to do with Kate?"

"Wait — while you were away Mr. Walsh, I asked John Padden to deliver the ring of engagement to Kate. He was in our store and said he had a delivery for your mother, and I asked him to deliver a box. That was weeks ago. Kate has never said a word of it. I don't believe she ever received it. I think he may have stolen it or sold it, never having any intentions of getting it to Kate. Now I understand why she never thanked me — she never got it. I want to see this John Padden, sir. Will you come with me? Shall we see if that is where Kate was off to?"

"I know John Padden, Colm. He is no thief."

"Sean, come with Colm and me. We've some searching to do. We shall be back here tomorrow with Ellen to see the baby, but, right now, we've got to go. Aunt Biddy will be minding Honor."

The three men climbed into the large *currach* and headed in the direction Kate had been seen. With the three of them rowing, the time would go by fast. But it was enough time for Colm to put John Padden in a bad light. Padraig was beginning to think the worst. He was angry that none of this had been mentioned to him. What was his daughter thinking?

As they approached Tullagh Bay, they could see another boat moving toward the lighthouse. Colm could tell it was towing his boat. There were two figures in the lead boat.

"That must be them, Mr. Walsh. That must be Padden and your daughter — I see my boat being hauled."

They changed course and followed; now they were all headed toward Inishkea.

"I see a boat following us, Kate. Who would it be?"

Kate turned and looked. It was still a bit of a distance, but she recognized her Da and Sean. But there was also a third person.

"God, no! 'Tis my Da, for sure, with Sean, and there is another man in the boat. I'm afraid it might be Colm Mahon — it is his boat I stole."

John and Kate arrived at the harbor first. John pulled his *currach* to the side, untied the small boat, and pushed it onto the shore.

The other boat was close behind. Colm was the first out and went straight for John. He got in the first punch and knocked John to the ground.

Kate tried to intervene but was stopped by her father.

"Let 'em fight, Kate. There must be some reason for all this nonsense, and I think you might have too much to do with it. What have you been doing while your father was away? Pray, tell me, child."

"Da, please make them stop. I don't want John hurt."

"So, 'tis Padden you care about, then — not Colm Mahon?"

"Yes, Da, I am in love with John Padden. I've no feelings for Colm."

Padraig and Sean broke up the fight after letting Colm get in a few good punches. It appeared John Padden didn't want to fight back.

"Padden, where is the box I asked you to deliver to Kate? Have you sold it?"

"Ask Kate yourself, Mahon. She knows the bloody thing is on this island."

"Yes, 'tis true, but I would not accept it. So I asked John to hide it somewhere safe until I could give it back to you. I was waiting for Da to return home."

"I do not want your gift, Colm. I don't want any-thing from you!" Kate spat these words from her mouth as if they were bitter fruit.
"Daughter, *I* am to decide that. Now, come — let us find that box. John, go and get it from where it

is hidden, and pray it be there."

Soon, there was another person walking toward the harbor. It was Kate's mother.

"What news is there of Honor and the baby?"

Sean was the first to speak up. "Oh, Mum, you are a Grandmother of a fine boy! Honor has had the baby and is in a good way. And I am a proud Father!"

"We are to celebrate, for certain. But, please tell me: What is going on here?"

"Ellen, take this daughter of ours home. I will be there shortly. We have something to set right with these men; we'll get this sorted now. Go — I won't be long."

Kate's mum took her arm. She wanted to stay, to defend her John. But her Da was angry, and she knew better than to go against his demands. As she walked toward home, she saw John emerge from the cliffs with the box in his hands.

"That's it!" Colm shouted. "Mr. Walsh, that box has the ring declaring marriage to Kate."

"I don't know why you did not deliver this to my daughter, Padden, but there sure must be something here between you and Colm. I hope it is not about my daughter. You've had my respect, John Padden. You've been coming to this island for many a year, but today may be the last. Now, go."

"Sean, allow Colm to stay in your cottage tonight. We can settle this tomorrow. Right now, we should be celebrating with a drop or two."

"Surely, I'm weary and delighted anyway, Padraig. Tomorrow, we will get Colm back to Belmullet and on to the hospital. I'll see my dear Honor and child."

"'Tis right by you, Colm, to stay and take some *poteen* with us?"

Colm was inspecting his precious little box.
"What is it you're asking, Sean? Stay? Have some? Why, yes — some *poteen* would be grand."
Quietly, John rowed away, into the darkness.

CHAPTER THIRTEEN

Diary: December 15, 1880

I've been stuck on this island for too many days now. Da has not allowed me to leave, even to visit Honor. He has refused to talk to me. He is still trying to decide how to punish me, I guess. And I've no way to contact John.

What am I to do? How can I tell Mum and Da about my carrying a baby? Da will be furious, for sure, and I'll break Mum's heart — unless they would be so happy to have another grandchild so soon. They are so happy and proud of little Paddy.

Honor and the baby will be coming back to Inishkea tomorrow with Uncle Thomas.

Thomas and Biddy Geraghty arrived the next day with Honor and the new grandson, Paddy. They were met at the harbor by all of the family, except for Kate. Her father would not allow her to leave the house. It was heartbreaking for her — she loved her sister so much, as she loved all of her family. But the man she loved was gone. Was she ever to see him again?

Before they returned to the mainland, Aunt Biddy came to the cottage to visit her God- daughter Kate. She was aware of the troubles and wanted to offer some support.

"Kate, darling, I've come to see you, and I have an offer for you that may change things around here. I've talked to your Da, and he agrees that it would be good for you to come to stay with me and Uncle Thomas. You will be near town, and you can be with people your age. He would like you to start courting Colm, but that can wait. I know you are upset with all that has happened. I don't understand it all myself, but it will give us time to talk, and I would love to have ya in my house. Surely, you will be good company — I miss my Maureen so."

Kate hugged her aunt and began sobbing.

"All will be sorted out soon, Kate. Now go and pack some things, and meet us at the harbor.

Your Uncle and I will be leaving soon."

As Kate was putting her things in a bundle, so many thoughts were in her head. There was the possibility she would see John in town. She could tell him it would all be right if they got married. Even if he didn't want to marry, she was willing to run off with him. She knew she would bring shame to her family when they learned she was pregnant. And even if they did allow her to marry, Colm Mahon surely would no longer want her. She never cared to see him again, ever.

Only her mum came to the landing with her Aunt and Uncle. Padraig would stay away once again. He was a proud man.

Her mum said, "Kate, will ya please be a good girl now? You'll be happy there on the mainland, I'm sure. I think you may need to be away from Inishkea for a while." Crying, she hugged and kissed her daughter goodbye.

As they left the island behind, Kate watched as Inishkea disappeared farther and farther into the distance. She thought of how big a place it had once been to her. How she would ride "Pint" through the fields. How she walked with the sheep close to the cliffs, getting herself wet with the ocean spray. She could see the baby seals, the nests of hawks, the wild geese flocks flying over her home. But it was to end. It would never be the same again, never be her island. Aunt Biddy could see the tears in her eyes.

"Girl, don't be so sad, now. Ya can always go back. Your Da will forgive ya in time. He's one stubborn man, me brother. He still loves you, and things will be fine soon. You need a good time in town — that's what I'm a'thinking. When was the last time ya were dancing? Thomas and I go to the 'Ceili' dances[2] once a month, but they have them more often than that. And if it's not Colm Mahon ya want to see, there'll be plenty of other boys who would be dancing with ya."

[2] Folk dances

CHAPTER FOURTEEN

Diary: December 20, 1880

I've been trying to get up my nerve for talking to Aunt Biddy about my "situation." Tomorrow, we plan to do the Christmas baking, so I'll be in the house all day with my Godmother. It's time I tell her; please, God — let her forgive me!

"Good morning to ya, Kate. Surely, we've got us some work to be doing today. I'm looking forward to it. Ah, the smell of bread and the cookies! We'll be making dozens of them. They'll be able to smell me oven in Galway!"

"Now, don't be looking so sad and teary eyed. I think your Da will be forgiving ye as a Christmas present. Sure, he's over being angry with ya by now. And he and your mum will probably be visiting us some time in the next few days. You'll see — he'll be hugging and kissin' on ya again."

"Aunt Biddy, if I was to be in some kind of trouble, would you stand by me?"

"Sure — haven't I been doing that for ye whole life, Kate?"

"So, if I told you something I knew would make my Da upset, you would not be angry with me?"

"Well, girl, what is it?"

"You may want to sit down, Aunt Biddy."

Biddy set aside the sack of flour and sat down next to the hearth.

Kate sat next to her and took her hands in hers. "Aunt Biddy ... Godmother, I am with child."

"Oh, Jaysus, Mary, and Joseph, Kate!"

"Ye are pregnant? How and when did this all come about? I've no notice of ya being so. When could this have happened to ya?"

"It was so when I came here to your house, Aunt Biddy. 'Tis a secret I've had for almost three months now. 'Twas the reason I didn't want to marry Colm Mahon. I'm in love with the father of my baby, John Padden."

Biddy slumped into the chair. Kate could see the tears welling up in her eyes.

"Please don't cry, Aunt Biddy. Don't be sad — I'm not. I will be as happy as Honor when I have this baby, I will."

"Kate, answer me this: Did John Padden hurt ya? Did he take advantage of ya?"

"No, no — I was a willing woman. I'm in love with John, and I think he loves me. That is why I went to see him in Tullagh Bay. I went to tell him. I went there to stay with him, so we could get married."

"And what did John say to that, Kate?"

"Oh, he is afraid to marry; he has that sickness, which does not scare me at all. The 'falling sickness,' they call it. I've seen it happen to him, but I can be there for him. I want to be there to take care of him."

"Then, why has he not been here to see ya, Kate? Why does he not take responsibility for his actions? He should be showing more respect for ye. And your Da and Mum know nothing about this?"

"No — I hadn't the courage to tell them. I knew their hearts will be broken. If I could just get them to forgive John ... but he has deserted me; I don't know what to do. That is why I had to tell you. If it upsets you or shames you, I will leave. I can go to the convent in Galway or the workhouse in Belmullet to live."

"To the workhouse? Not me God-daughter! No, Kate, I will keep ya here with me. Now I will have to tell Padraig and Ellen all of this. I don't know what they will do. But you can be with me. I'll stand by ya."

They hugged each other and wiped each other's tears from their faces. It was told — no longer a secret. Now, for the reactions of her parents. Thank God for the love of Aunt Biddy.

Kate's parents came to visit. She stayed in her

room while Aunt Biddy talked to them alone. She knew she would be telling them of her pregnancy, and she didn't want to be there when her father was told — he would be ashamed, indeed. Her mother would be more forgiving, but it would be up to her Da to make the decision of what was to happen. There was a knock on her bedroom door, and Kate went to open it.

It was her father. He looked stern but had tears in his eyes. He asked Kate to sit down.

"I can hardly believe what I've just been told. I don't want to believe what I've just been told. But it is the truth — is it not?"

"Da, I wanted to tell you..."

"No, you did not want to tell me — that is what I know. You've been a good child, but even your mum thought I let you go a bit wild. Letting you roam the island — you were more like a son to me than a daughter. Why, I let you take care of the sheep and help birth the lambs! I didn't think I was putting these independent thoughts in your head. You have shamed the family.

"You should have told me a long time ago that Mahon was not the husband for you. I think he is a fine choice, but there is no way he will want you now.

"So your mother and I are hurt, but I am also angry. Is it true that the father of this child is John Padden?"

"Yes, Da, I'm in love with him ... and ... "

"No, you can't be in love with that man. I'll not have it. I'll not allow you to ever see him again. I've got to think. I'll need some time to decide what to do about this matter."

"But, Da, if you went and talked to John, perhaps he will ask you for my hand. Perhaps he will marry me!"

"I'll not let that happen, Kate. I'd rather see the man dead than married to my daughter."
"Oh, Da, no — please, no!"

"You are to do what I say, Kate Walsh. You'll stay here with your Godmother until the baby is born; then I will decide what to do. Your Mum and I were going to take you back to Inishkea today, but that will not happen now. You stay here, and think about what you have done. Not just to me and your mother, but to your own life, and now the life of a child. I'll tell your Mum to come in and say goodbye to you."

Kate jumped up into her mother's arms. They were both crying now.

"Kate, oh, Kate — what have you done? What has happened to ye, my daughter, my child?"

"I'm a woman, Mum, just like Honor. I can give you a grandchild! Will that not make you happy?"

"No, you've shamed your father, and you've hurt me. I don't know what he will do. But I love you still. And I thank God for Biddy — she loves you as well. At least you will have a home. I'm hoping you'll not end up in the workhouse. Do all ye can for Thomas and Biddy; they've been good to you and supporting as well. I've got to leave now. Your Da will be wanting to go, and he'll be thinking of what to do with you."

"But, Mum, could I not come back to Inishkea with my child and live? Maybe there will be an empty cottage soon, or I can stay with Gram, if she'll have me?"

"Kate, no, I will not ask that of your Grand-mum. Your Da will have to decide. 'Tis in his hands now, Kate. And you will have to abide by it. I love you, my daughter. I don't know when I will see you again, but know always that I love you with all my heart."

Kate was kneeling beside her Mother, crying. She had never felt such a deep sorrow. It was as if someone or something had died. She did not want to let go of her Mother. She thought she would never see her again.

Her mother rose from the chair and brought Kate to her. They hugged once again. Then Ellen took Kate's arms from around her and slowly backed away. She wiped the tears from her eyes and, without looking back, closed the door behind her.

CHAPTER FIFTEEN

Diary: February 17, 1881

I went down to the strand tonight to watch the sunset over Inishkea, as I do so many nights now. It is not a far walk to the beach from the cottage. Guess if I had "Pint" here, I would have rode him down to where the *currachs* are. Uncle Thomas and many of his neighbors have their boats stacked together, even tied to each other. It keeps them from getting pulled out to sea.

The weather is getting warmer now. Spring is near. I took my boots off and walked on the soft sand; it felt good.

I heard voices and the sound of horses coming down the beach, so I went and sat out of the way, near a *currach*. It was Colm and Nora Duffy riding the strand. I didn't have time to hide, as I wished I could. But he saw me there — they both did — and continued to ride by laughing and saying a thing or two. After they got a bit past where I was sitting, I could hear Colm say something, and they laughed again. I just know it was about me. I know I will carry this shame with me forever, unless John comes and makes me respectable with marriage. But I don't hear a word about him. I believe he must have left Tullagh. I go to town often with Uncle Thomas, and I never see him or even hear his name mentioned.

Uncle Thomas delivers fish to the market a few times a week, and I always go to lend a hand. Aunt Biddy would rather stay at home. She bakes a lot of bread that we sell at market.

I miss my family so much. I miss my island, I miss "Pint," and I miss home. Da has not yet forgiven me. It hurts so not to see Honor and her baby. I miss Mum, and I fear I may never see Gram again; she is so old now.

My hope is that they will forgive me and have me come back home after they see my baby. I think that will make Da happy. *Please forgive me, God.*

CHAPTER SIXTEEN

April 14, 1881

"Good morning, Aunt Biddy. What is all this food you're putting in the basket? Are you going on a picnic?"

"Very funny, Kate. No — this is for Thomas and the other fisherman going out today. They'll be gone till dark, so I've packed plenty of bread and cheese and some smoked fish for them. This is that time of year they go out past Inishglora for the lobster, and there will be at least eight boats."

"Well, they will all be in the safe hands of Saint Brendan, as the ruins of his church are still out there on Inishglora. I've seen them once; Da took me there a few years ago. He asked me to fish with him then. Now, I guess Anthony is old enough to go."

"And you know the tale of the 'Children of Lir'; they are still out there as well!"

"Yes, Auntie — their jealous stepmother turned

them into swans because she thought their father loved them too much — more than he loved her. For hundreds of years, they were these lovely birds. But when they heard Saint Brendan's church bells, they were turned back into humans, and he baptized them!"

"Right you are, Kate, but, by then, they were old and soon died. They are supposed to be buried on Inishglora. What a fine tale it is."

The day started out as a cloudless, sun-filled one, but, by afternoon, the sky had darkened, and the wind had become fierce. It was not a good time to be on the sea — not the North Atlantic — and there were eight *currachs*, light-weight open boats, full of men, out there.

Groups of women from the nearby cottages began to gather along the shore. A fire was built out of dried wood and grasses to provide a signal for the men. The sky was black now, with ugly, rolling clouds and gale-force winds. Many of the women went back to their homes to pray.

"Come, please, Aunt Biddy — we must go back inside. You're soaked with the rain and blowing sea. The men are the best fishermen and the best seamen in County Mayo. They will be safe. Perhaps they are all on Inishglora and will return in the morning. Come home now, Auntie, please."

"You're right Kate — he'll be back. I'll bet they are all sitting in a monk's cell, drinking the *poteen*. Damn them for making us worry. Let's be off, then."

Then next morning, the crowd was once again at the strand. It had been a terrible storm that lasted most of the night. Roofs were blown off, and fences were down. Animals were roaming all over the area. They could be caught later; they wouldn't go far. Right now, all eyes were on the horizon. Someone with a "glass" called out that there was a boat seen coming from the south. Then a few more were spotted in the north.

By mid-afternoon, there were five boats safe but three yet to be seen. Uncle Thomas's boat was not yet back. He had two other fishermen with him; the families stood together, holding hands and praying. The men who made it back told of the horror it was that night. Gale-force winds came up suddenly, and two boats capsized in the dark. A few were able to stay together using fishing line to tie themselves to each other. But the waves were so fierce that they could not see the other men. Their shouting voices were lost in the howling of the winds.

Larger fishing vessels were sent out from Blacksod to search. They found smashed boats on Inishglora and a few bodies on the rocks. They headed back toward the town harbor when night fell.

The families of the missing men began walking toward town. Only then would they find out who had been rescued and who had been lost.

Aunt Biddy, Mrs. Reilly, Mrs. Cawley, and Kate took the pony cart into town. It was dark by the time they arrived. The harbor was full of people — family and friends of the fishermen. It was a terrible sight. The bodies of four men were laid out on pallets of grain, waiting to be claimed.

Kate stayed next to her aunt. They held hands, and their free hand held rosary beads.

One of the four bodies was Uncle Thomas.

There was no consoling the woman, so deep was the pain of her terrible loss. Uncle Thomas had drowned; his body hadn't any blood on it. He looked as if he could have died in his sleep. Bless him!

The other men's bodies were bloody and broken. They had been thrown onto the rocks.

Kate and Mrs. Cawley managed to get Aunt Biddy back to the cart for the slow ride home. The bodies of the dead men were brought to the coroner's building, where they would be examined. The family members would all be there again early in the morning to carry their loved ones home, where the wakes would be held. News of the deaths traveled throughout the area, and, the next day, Kate was to see her Mum and Da. After months of silence, perhaps, now, they would talk to her.

Diary: April 14, 1881

I don't understand God. Why does he allow people to suffer and die? Today, my Uncle Thomas was found dead; he never made it back from the sea. We are all destroyed with grief. I cannot console Aunt Biddy. If only Maureen were here to be with her mother at this time. But she is far away in America. I hope my parents will come, and I hope they will talk to me. Perhaps, now, they will ask me to come back home.

The following day, there were to be three wakes within the small gathering of cottages by the strand. The Geraghty home, the Reillys, and the McGintys had all had lost a man of the family. Mrs. Reilly would be left with three children, and the McGinty family had lost their only son. With Thomas Geraghty's daughter in America, Biddy would be left alone — if it were not for the presence of Kate Walsh.

Kate sat next to her Aunt Biddy as people came by the home to say their goodbyes and pay their respects to Thomas Geraghty.

When Kate's parents came in the door, she stood up to greet them, hoping they would open their arms to her.

But Padraig and Ellen went directly to Biddy upon entering the house. It was she who would be approached first, out of respect for Thomas.

It was then her parents would speak with Kate.

"Darling Kate." Her Mum was the first to approach her. "I've missed you so, and now this! What is happening to our lives? They are being torn apart with grief! "

"But how are you getting on? Are you well? Your Da is going to speak to you today. I don't know exactly what he is going to say, but I feel his heart has been softened. I know he loves and misses you like we all do. He is just very good at not showing it. But I can see it — I know him. I hope, please God, that he will let you come home, back home to Inishkea. But, now, with this happening, what are we to do with your Aunt Biddy? She should not be alone, and, ah! — with Maureen so far away, she surely will need someone with her."

"Hello, Da."

Padraig, with tears in his eyes, pulled Kate to him. He hugged his daughter for the first time in months. They were both crying now. Kate looked at her Mum; she was crying as well.

"Kate, my daughter, my sweet daughter, I've missed you so. I am sorry I am the man I am; I should be standing by you instead of pushing you away. But you've hurt my pride, my reputation as a big man — the Master of Inishkea. I'm sorry to hurt you this way. With the death of Thomas, it just breaks the family into more bits."

Padraig left Kate and gathered his sister into his strong arms. They stood in this embrace for some time, both crying tears of loss and regret.

"Oh, my poor Bridget, my poor sister — we will all miss your good man Thomas."

The burial took place the following day. They were to be buried at Saint Deirbhile's cemetery in Falmore, next to the sea — a place where the men worked, a place the men loved, the sea that took their lives.

Her parents had told Kate they loved her, but there was not a word said about her going to Inishkea. Kate stayed with her Aunt. She would see her Mum and Honor only when they came to visit, which was not very often.

The spring turned into summer, a beautiful Ireland summer. The land was green with lush grasses, and the sky was a beautiful blue, like the eyes of the Irish.

Kate was showing her pregnancy now. There was no wearing her Da's breeches! She had to make some clothes to fit her growing body. Honor had given her a few dresses as well.

But Aunt Biddy was never happy again. She was hardly speaking these days. It had been hard for her to see her daughter go off to America, and now she had lost her husband of many years. It was a rare time when Kate would see a smile on the face of Aunt Biddy.

Diary: May 19, 1881

The chores are getting to be too much for me to do alone. Uncle Thomas's sister lives nearby and comes in to check on both Aunt Biddy and me, but my pregnancy has become a burden to them. I heard Mum and Aunt Biddy talking in whispers. I could hear the word "workhouse." I think that is where I shall be going. Once I have the baby, I can stay on there and work in the laundry. The nuns will take care of the baby while I do the chores required of me. Perhaps I will find happiness there. Once my baby is born, I will have love once again in my life.

CHAPTER SEVENTEEN

One of the ways to acquire money was to make and sell *Poteen.* Inishkea was quite well known for its quality whiskey. Padraig Walsh was one of the best-known distillers. The fresh water from the holy wells and quality barley from his fields were the secrets. His copper still and many of his neighbor's stills were hidden in the caves on the western side of the island. It was illegal to make and sell whiskey in those days, but that did not stop its production. Some of Padraig Walsh's best customers were clergymen, of both persuasions, and court officials — providing they were Irish, not English.

Padraig walked to the Burkes' cottage to ask for a favor. He needed to get his whiskey to the mainland, and the best way to disguise it was in creels. These wicker baskets normally were used to carry fish or turf, and two could be put on the back of a donkey from the boat to Belmullet.

"Good evening to you all. Billy and Mrs. Burke, how are you getting on? I've not seen you out much these days. Are you all doing well?"

"Hello! Cheers, Padraig, my friend! Come in now, come in, and help ye'self to me first batch of *Poteen!*"

"Well, Billy, it is certainly a large quantity you have. You've done a good job, once again!"

"Mr. Walsh, 'tis not the quality of yer own. We didn't have the good barley this year — but it still does the trick! Billy here is proof of that. He's been sitting here in a sea of blaggardism, he has."

"Oh, herself is just thinking I'm not a daycint man, on account of me drinking so much today. But Padraig, did ya know me family is one that lived in castles? There is one there in Ballina, the castle of my ansisthers who were my four fathers."

"How," said Mrs. Burke, "could your aunt's sisters be your four fathers? And is that big mass of water out there yer moat? The one we call the Atlantic?"

"I was after telling ya, that I come from a King's family, and ya don't wan a listen. Come Padraig — you sits and 'ave a glass with me. I know you'll be b'layving me."

"Well, I'd love to sit down with you, Billy, but I've got to be continuing on. I just want to borrow some of your creels. I'll need them to take some things to the mainland tomorrow."

"Oh, sure, sure — just help ye'self to what ya need Padraig, I'll not be goin' anywhere for a few days, it looks to me! Ya sure ye don' be needn' a drop?"

Padraig went to their shed and pulled out four creel baskets. Each basket would hold at least eight bottles of his *Poteen.* There were plenty of buyers for the whiskey. Besides the clergy, the "Shebeens" were good customers. These pubs did not have a license to sell but did so anyway, at the risk of being caught by the government "regulators."

Padraig had a plan — one which would have a great bearing on Kate's future. He was going to talk to the priest, Father McHale. He was a *Poteen* customer, and he also had a lot to do with the workhouse. If the priest would agree, Kate would be placed there in the workhouse to have her baby. Usually only those without any means of paying were allowed to enter the workhouse, but perhaps he could use a bit of bribery to get the priest to allow her in. It would be easier on his sister Bridget not to have a pregnant girl in the house. She was barely able to take care of herself, let alone deliver a baby!

In Belmullet, it was agreed.

CHAPTER EIGHTEEN

The workhouse was an austere place, and the rules were strict. Everyone was awakened at 6:00 am; they worked until breakfast at 8:30. Work again until lunch at 2:00 pm and dinner at 6:00. It was back in the rooms at 8:00 pm and lights out. All worked for room and board — "three hots and a cot" was the expression.

The boys did all the outside work, tending to the animals and chickens, patching roofs, mending fences, and building gates.

Most of the girls worked in the laundry: washing, ironing, and sewing. The workhouse was paid to do these tasks by the local hospital, the Erris Hotel, and the few wealthy people in the area. The women also did all the cooking and cleaning.

The only people to be seen from outside the workhouse were the turf and linen deliverymen.

There was also the nursery, where the babies and younger children were housed. That was the best place to work, though the oldest women were placed there. Those who had children in the nursery were not able to see them until the day's end, after the chores were finished and after 6:00 pm dinner. Many of them would pass on having something to eat just so they could be with their children until 8:00 pm.

Kate worked in the kitchen, peeling potatoes and vegetables while sitting; this she would do until the baby was born. The women who worked in the kitchen were of various ages. Many of the older women had lived in the workhouse for many years; they could be hard and cruel to the others. The younger ones were quiet and sad, as was Kate.

She made very few friends there in the time before the baby arrived. Kate was alone during the delivery; her family had not come, nor was this encouraged by the Sisters of Mercy.

It was a painful, frightening experience, but once the baby was placed in Kate's arms, she forgot it all.

A beautiful baby girl! Kate was so happy: crying and laughing at the same time. What a wondrous creature she was. So tiny and pink! And she was healthy; that was the main concern. Kate was allowed to keep the baby with her for a few hours, until the caretakers from the nursery came.

"Please, may I keep her with me for the night? I want so much to have her here next to me."

Kate was allowed to stay in the nursery area for three days, and then it was back to the dormitory and back to work. She was given time to nurse the baby several times a day. It was a joyous time for her; Kate never felt so happy in all her days.

"Sweet baby girl; I shall name you Mary, like the Holy Mother. I hope to have more people love you as I do; your grandparents, and aunts and uncles. And you will have a cousin to meet, little Paddy. I hope Honor and all of the family will come to visit us soon. I am sure they will love you."

Padraig Walsh had made some other plans for Kate and little Mary. He had promised that the child would be put up for adoption after its first birthday. The workhouse had arrangements with an adoption center in Galway called the "Bird's Nest." Children were sold there.

Kate was not aware of these plans. She had hoped that she would return to Inishkea with her baby. Surely her Da would want his first Granddaughter to be there at home.

Diary: June 19, 1881

My baby, Mary, is beautiful and healthy. I am so happy now that she is with me. I felt so alone all those months, not having John in my life. There has never been a word from him; I do not know where he can be. And Mum and Da have not come to visit. I hope to see Aunt Biddy soon, and Honor. I so wish they would come.

Father McHale shall be here this week, and I need to talk with him. I so want to have Mary baptized, although the church does not allow it. If only John would come to me to be married. But I shall ask Father McHale. He is a friend of my Da's; maybe

that will persuade him. Then I must ask Aunt Biddy, my Godmother, to be the same for little Mary.

CHAPTER NINETEEN

Father McHale would not baptize an illegitimate child — except for the favors he owed Padraig Walsh. A stock of *poteen* in the church rectory was reason enough to accommodate Walsh's request. But he refused to have the ceremony in the church; the holy well would have to do.

Aunt Biddy was given permission from the Master of the workhouse, Mr. Maxwell, for Kate and her baby to be away for a few hours. They were to meet Father McHale in Falmore. No other family member would attend. Father McHale was in quite a hurry and beckoned them to gather around him. He had Aunt Biddy, the Godmother, hold the baby while he poured "holy water" on her forehead. "I baptize thee, Mary Magdalen, in the name of the Father, Son, and Holy Spirit."

A bit of a gasp came from Biddy, but she dare not say a thing to the priest.

Kate was surprised, as she hadn't chosen "Magdalen" for a middle name, but it was quite nice:

Mary Magdalen.

The ceremony was quickly over, and the priest was on his way. Kate, Mary, and their Godmother walked to the donkey cart.

"Aunt Biddy, do you think Da and Mum would have me come home? I miss them so much, and I miss Inishkea, my Island home!"

"I'm afraid your Da will not allow that, Kate. He's not yet said what he will do, but your Mum tells me she asks him all the time, if he will allow ya to come home. You know he can be a stubborn man."

"I pray to God that he will change his mind. If he would just look upon Mary, he would love her — do you not think so?"

"I agree Kate, perhaps 'tis why he has stayed away — does not want to appear 'soft'!"

"But, we must be on our way; I shall come to see ya again. Do not give up hope. Enjoy your daughter; she's lovely, and a blessing to your life."

Upon entering the workhouse, the women from the nursery were ready to take the baby. It was heartbreaking to give her up. It was difficult to let her go and return to the dormitory. She had to work in the kitchen still, so off with her better clothes, and back into the grey uniform of work.

Late that evening, while lying in bed, Kate could not help but cry. It felt like a heavy stone was placed on her chest, it was the loneliness of not having her loved ones in her life. What love she did have was in a different room in the workhouse — her Mary, Mary Magdalen. Without her, there was no life at all.

"Katie, are you OK?" asked Anne from the next bed.

"Oh, yes, Anne, I'm fine, but I am so lonely. I miss my family, miss living on my island, and especially miss my baby so. Don't you miss little Michael?"

"I do, but I have no choice in the way things are

here. There are rules, and I follow them. Besides, I am so tired at the end of the day; I wouldn't want Michael's crying keeping me up all hours!"

"Oh, I hope Mary isn't in that nursery crying. I hope they hold her, rock her, and kiss her. They do comfort the children, don't they?"

"I don't think the women want to be up at night rocking babies. They would be putting cotton in their ears, they would, just so as not to hear."

"Well, I soon hope to be gone from here, and I will take good care of my Mary. I won't let her cry and be lonely — never, never."

"Once she is adopted, she will probably have caring parents," added Anne. "They wait a long time to get our babies; I think they are probably good mothers — although some of the rich hire other women to raise them."

"What is that you are saying, girl? My baby is not for adoption! Where did you hear such a story as this?"

"Everyone knows the children do not stay here long; they send them to Galway. Michael will be going soon. He is almost a year now; that's when they take them away."

The next day Kate tried to talk to Mr. Maxwell. The matron told her she would have to wait until he had time for her.

A few days later, she was called to his office.

"Sir, I have a question about my child."

"Yes, go on, go on. What is it, now? I'm a very busy man here."

"Well, Sir, I was wondering when I will be allowed to take my baby back to Inishkea?"

"Where...oh, out there? Absolutely not, miss! What has given you this idea that you are leaving, with a baby no less!"

"I am just waiting for my parents to come for us; —me and Mary, my baby."

"You've no idea of what happens here, do you? Most of these children leave; they are to be given to good parents, but I don't imagine you will be going anytime soon. Where are you to go? You're parents have not told me they want you home. You have shamed your family, girl, and your child needs two parents — a man and his wife — to take care of it. You are not fit to be a mother. Now see the time? We are finished here!"

"I will not give up my child! Who are you conspiring with, Sir? I was never told you planned to do this."

"Well, your father surely knows. He and Father McHale spoke to me about it prior to you coming here. Your baby goes up for adoption after its first birthday."

"No, no — that cannot be! My father, you say, arranged this?"

"It is what we do here. We find good homes for children of sinners, fallen women that you are.

148

"Now, out of my office, and get back to your work."

CHAPTER TWENTY

There were more tears that night, but Kate was angry as well. She did not want to believe that her own father would give away his granddaughter. She was not going to allow that to happen. Thoughts of how to run away entered her mind. How could she get to the nursery and get Mary, and be gone from this place? But where, where could she go? She was afraid of her father and what he could do. He never answered any of her letters, and now she wondered if her mother ever got to read them. Maybe the letters had been destroyed.

Aunt Biddy — she was Kate's only hope. Kate wrote a letter telling her Aunt of the adoption plan made by her father. She pleaded with Aunt Biddy to take her in. Any letter posted from the workhouse would be read by the Matron or Mr. Maxwell, so Kate would find another way to get it to her Aunt. She knew one of the turf delivery boys, a neighbor of the Geraghtys. She planned to pass the letter to him the next delivery day. She folded the letter and put it in her apron pocket.

Several days went by without any word from her Godmother; she had to be patient.

Bridget sat and read the letter once again. She had not been aware of her brother wanting to give up Kate's child for adoption. *How hardhearted that would be,* she thought. With her own daughter, Maureen, so far away, she felt Kate was like a daughter to her now. She would never allow a Godchild of hers to be given away. She knew many of the children adopted were to be brought up in that other religion and to be used as maids in their English homes.

Biddy made a decision: It had been too lonely in the house. She had grieved for months and would not stop grieving for Thomas, but she felt stronger. Now she wanted to help her Godchildren!

Word got to Padraig and Ellen that Bridget was willing to have Kate come and live with her — and not only Kate but Mary Magdalen as well. There was no way she was going to allow a God-daughter of hers to be sold to the "Birds Nest" in Galway. Padraig begrudgingly told Ellen about his "deal" with Father McHale. Kate's mother was shocked; she never thought her husband would do such a thing. She agreed with Bridget that Kate and the baby should leave that horrible place. She had made a mistake, yes, lost her innocence, but she should not lose her child as well!

One morning, a delivery cart arrived at the workhouse back door. It was Joseph Reilly, the neighbor of Aunt Biddy's who had taken Kate's letter. He motioned to Kate to come near, and, when she did, he passed an envelope to her, telling her to keep quiet. When she was in her bed that night, she read the letter. Aunt Biddy wanted Kate out of that horrible place, and she had a plan. On Sunday next at noon, she was to walk to the northern gate of the yard, with Mary Magdalen, and a cart would be there waiting for them.

Kate was to leave the workhouse. No permission was needed from Mr. Maxwell — she was going. Aunt Biddy would come! That Sunday, Kate walked with Mary through the garden and back toward the stables — the North gate. She had told no one of her plan. She would soon be free.

Aunt Biddy and Joseph Reilly arrived in a cart. Kate was waiting outside the workhouse walls with her baby in her arms. There had not been such a happy day since Mary was born!

"Aunt Biddy, I love you so much. Thank you, thank you. We will bring joy to you. Just look at this beautiful girl I hold. There will be laughter in your home once again. And love — yes! We will all be in love, thank God!"

Diary: February 27, 1882

Dear God, thank you. Thank you for the home I now have — a home with my child and my loving Aunt. We are going to be happy here. I will work hard to be sure that I am not a burden to my dear Aunt. She seems to be happy now; she smiles and laughs, as do I. My little girl has brought joy to us all. I have not yet seen Mum, but I hope she will visit soon. I don't know what I will do if I see my father. How can I ever forget he was going to give away my child?

The Geraghty home turned into a happy one.

Little Mary was a joy to both Kate and her Aunt Biddy. Days turned into weeks and weeks into a year. Mary was walking and talking now, and she seemed such a happy little girl.

Aunt Biddy had days of sorrow, and she would go off and sit on the strand, staring out to sea. It was her quiet time with Thomas. Kate would get a fire going with the turf and make dinner, allowing Biddy to have the time she needed to be alone.

They had been able to care for each other as well. Kate was a talented seamstress and made clothes to be sold in town. She also sold goods at market. Her sister Honor came to visit once a month, bringing her son Paddy. Honor was the only connection Kate had now with Inishkea. But Honor told Kate that she felt their Mum wanted to see her and her granddaughter Mary. She may come and visit, without Padraig knowing, as he had still not forgiven his daughter.

June 1885

Aunt Biddy and Kate made a happy home together. Kate had been making gifts for her daughter's birthday and was almost finished with the miniature horse made of wool. Aunt Biddy had sewn a lovely coat and bonnet for Mary. There were sweets made, and company was expected: Kate's mother was to visit. Honor and Sean were to come from Inishkea with her. This would be the first time Mary would see her grandmother and for her grandmother to see her only granddaughter!

"You are to receive a grand present for your birthday, Mary. You have heard me tell you of my Mum. Your Grandmother is coming here to visit."

Kate kept looking out of the window, watching for the cart with her family to come up the South road. She was so excited to see her mother. Oh, if only her father would come as well — then all would be perfect. What would she do if they asked her to return to Inishkea? She had given that a lot of thought and decided it would be better to stay with her Aunt Biddy, although she was becoming quite independent these days. Kate brought in most of the money they lived on; they did not want for much.

Kate saw them coming; she wanted to meet them outside, wanted to greet her mother before little Mary was introduced.

It was a tearful meeting: they hugged and kissed, and both said how sorry they were. Kate felt forgiven and was so happy.

"Oh, Mum, now come and see your granddaughter Mary Magdalen. I tell her about you every night. In our prayers, you are her guardian angel."

"Hello, Mary, hello, sweet girl — I am your Grandmum! Oh, and you look just like your mother — look at those blond curls!"

There was much laughter and talking; it was a lovely day together. The hours sped by quickly, and it was time for them to leave. They had to get back to Inishkea before sunset.

"Mum, please talk to Da. Tell him to come and see his granddaughter. He will fall in love with her, I'm sure. Then maybe he will forgive me. I'm so sorry I brought him shame. And I'll not be asking to come back to Inishkea. No, I shall stay here — 'tis my home now."

"Kate, your Da has been planning something for quite some time. I found a tin he has been filling with money. He sold all of this year's *Poteen*, and the tin is full. I asked what he was to do with it all, and he says it has to do with you. I don't know what it is, but I think that it be a good sign. I know he still loves you and wants to do something good for you and Mary. Pray to God!"

The Ballina Journal,

And Connaught Advertiser.

THE BALLINA JOURNAL, MONDAY, FEBRUARY 25, 1886.

[Registered]   PRICE ONE PENNY

CHAPTER TWENTY-ONE

Ellen could not keep a secret from her husband. She had to tell him about her visit with their daughter.

Padraig listened patiently while his wife begged him to allow Kate to come home. If he would not allow it, then to please go and see her; see his beautiful granddaughter.

"Well, you had better sit yourself down, Ellen. I have been putting money aside so Kate and the child can go to America. I have written to my uncle, and he has room in his home for them both. It is best for them. They will be away from the shame, away from the talk, and away from me."

"Padraig! You don't mean to say, you have no desire to see the child, and no love for your own daughter? Are ye so proud a man, as to not let your own blood be here with us, near us?"

Ellen was crying now. But Padraig stood firm.

"She shall make a new life for herself ,Ellen. She is still young and can begin a new life. She will say her husband has died; no one will know the truth. No one has to."

"Oh, I can't bear it! I do not want you to send Kate away! Please, please go and see her. If you see them both, I believe you will change your mind."

"I won't do that. I cannot do that. This is difficult enough. I have thought of this for a long while. It is the best I can do for them. I have purchased passage for them on the Allen line. You shall deliver the news and the tickets to her yourself. I cannot see her."

"No, oh no Padraig, please don't make me send her off. And my granddaughter — I shall never see them again!"

"Tomorrow I will bring you to the mainland. You can go on by yourself to Biddy's house and deliver the tickets and the money I have saved for them."

It was to be. There would be no changing the mind

of Padraig Walsh. He knew his wife and daughter would think of him as cruel, but in his mind, it was the best for Kate. He also knew that, as "king" of Inishkea, he could not make the rules different for his own child. She must remain shunned.

The following day Padraig brought them to the mainland. He sent Ellen up the "south" road and on to the Geraghty house alone. He was to wait by the boat for her return. And she was to return alone!

Kate and Mary Magdalen were out playing in the fields when Ellen arrived. She had a chance to talk to Biddy alone. They both cried while she told of Padraig's plan for her daughter; it was heart breaking.

Kate and Mary entered the cottage and were taken by surprise, a pleasant surprise, to see Ellen.

"Oh, Mum, you've come to visit again. We are so happy to see you, aren't we Mary!"

"My Grand-mum! My Grand-mum has come to see me!"

"But what is it Mum? You have been crying, and you as well, Aunt Biddy. What is it? Has something happened to Da? To Honor or Paddy? Please say 'No'!"

"Kate, dear, please sit her next to me by the fire so we can talk. Biddy will keep an eye on Mary for a bit."

"It breaks my heart to tell ye this, but Da has made arrangements for you and Mary Magdalen to travel to America. Now don't be afraid — we have family there; an uncle of your father's can provide a place for you and your daughter, as soon as you arrive in Pennsylvania. It is said to be beautiful, with great rivers and high green mountains covered with tall trees. You will be happy there — I know it. And it will be a new start. You can get away from the small-minded people in this town and be a proud Walsh once again. And Mary will have no shame in her life, no people to be cruel to her."

"But, Mum, we've just been starting a new life here, with you....you and Da. Please say that is why you want me to stay. Cannot my own Da forgive me? Does he not love his own child and grandchild?"

"It must be, Kate. Your Da has made this decision, but I must abide. Please know I shall always love you, no matter where you are."

Tears were shed by all; even little Mary seemed to know something was wrong.

"Are you not going to be my guardian angel anymore, Grand-mum?"

"Oh, child, I am — I am still. But you must remember: I can watch over you without you seeing me,.I shall be there always, always."

CHAPTER TWENTY-TWO

Aunt Biddy loaded the cart with a basket of food she had prepared. It was full of cheese, apples, oat and rye cakes, hard-boiled eggs, smoked fish, tea, and bee's honey. She hoped it would be enough for a journey across the Atlantic. She was afraid for Kate and Mary and really did not want them to leave. But she knew not to go against her brother's wishes. And it was true: It would be a fresh start for Kate and Mary Magdalen. They could begin a new life, away from the hurtful gossip and shame Kate was being subjected to here.

As they rode together toward Blacksod Bay, they could see the ship, the Allen Liner, looming in the distance. It was a frightening, wondrous, exciting sight. Little Mary was pointing and asking many questions — which Aunt Biddy had to answer. Kate was silent, and tears ran down her face. As the trap drove down past the few neighbors waving from their cottages, Kate gave a weak wave in return. She looked at the beautiful setting — thatched-roof, whitewashed cottages along the dunes and strand. She could see the Celtic cross of Uncle Thomas' grave; that is when she sobbed openly.

As they approached the harbor, Kate could see Honor and Sean there, but she could not see her mother or father. There were hugs, kisses, and promises of letter writing amongst them. Sean paid two boys to carry the large basket and the small bundle of clothes to Kate's bunk on the ship. She would be sharing a bed with Mary in a dormitory just for the women and children.

Everything was happening so fast. She was afraid of the ship — not of the sea; her father had been a good teacher, and she was aware of the dangers and the beauty of the sea.

Kate took Mary Magdalen's hand and walked up the gangplank to the main deck. She handed their tickets to the agent.

"Say, woman, what's the name? I can't understand this Irish writing. I've got to put a name on the list here."

"The name — oh, it is Katherine, Katherine Padden, and this is my daughter, Mary Magdalen Padden. My husband has passed away — drowned in the same sea that I am about to cross. 'John,' yes, 'John Padden' was his name."

She found a place along the rail to look down upon her family waving goodbye. Kate lifted Mary so she could see over the crowd.

She could see her sister and Biddy, both crying now. It was heartbreaking, but she had to stop crying herself — it would frighten Mary. Little Mary Magdalen, poor girl, had no idea she would never see her family again.

From this height on the ship's deck, Kate could see the rooftops in Belmullet. *Good riddance to you,* she thought.

Ropes were tossed, and the great ship began to move away from the dock; many people left the deck and went below. But Kate wanted to stay and watch. She and Mary walked forward to a position allowing them an open view of the horizon in front of them. They were to pass between Duvillaun Mor Island and South Inishkea, heading west.

Duvillaun looked so small from this vantage point. Quickly, in her mind, she relived that day, the day she thought she found love — the man of her life. And deep inside, she still felt a longing for John, no matter what he had done; she still felt love for him.

As they approached Inishkea, she could see the expanse north toward the end of the island, the area where she used to ride "Pint" with all the freedom in the world. It was her island back then, hers to explore and to own. She would have imagined herself as an Irish Queen, and that was her domain.

Barely visible was the small church steeple on the North Island. She looked at the blanket of green, the small silver-grey of the houses and the bit of strand at the harbor.

As they moved past, she saw the rocky edge of

the south corner, the place she would wait to see John's boat coming from Tullagh Bay, the place she would sit and dream.

Now in sight was the southwest coast of the island — the high cliffs and rocks where the wild Atlantic would smash upon it. A place even she would fear but was brave enough to rescue a sheep from, if she had to — or wait for a man.

It was then she saw a figure, the shape of a man, standing near the cliff's edge. Her heart leapt! Was it John? But, no, that could not be. He had been banished from the island and had also not been seen for quite some time.

Her heart sank in her chest when she realized it was her Da. He had come to see her off, in his own way.

"Oh, Da, Da," she sobbed. "Why, why did you send me away? I've just wanted to come home, home to be with you and Mum, the people I love. We could have been so happy there on Inishkea with my baby, your granddaughter."

"Why are you crying, Mommy?"

"Oh, my sweet girl, I am crying because I am so happy. We are going on a big adventure and will have new people and things to see. I am not sad. I am happy to be with you, the girl I love."

Kate looked back and could barely see the figure, still standing there in the same spot where she saw her Da.

"Goodbye, dear Da. Please find a place in your heart to love us; we are yours and shall always be."

The Island was fading into an emerald green strip of land. Before them was a vast horizon of ocean. The sun was setting, and the sky was streaked with colors of gold and pink — a beautiful sight.

Mary grabbed her mother's hand and pulled her forward to get a better view.

"Look Mommy, look." Pointing toward the sunset, Mary Magdalen said, "Look how beautiful is America."

CHAPTER TWENTY-THREE
TULLAGH BAY

Anthony, Padraig's son, nineteen now and a tall strong man he had become. Anthony also had harbored a hatred for the man who caused his sister to leave Ireland.

There was a debt to be paid by John Padden, as he had broken the Walsh family. Padraig and Anthony took their *currach* out for a trip to Tullagh Bay, where they would find Padden. It was near dark when they saw his boat coming in toward the sand bar. They had dropped anchor as close to his cottage as they were able; Padraig laid low in the boat. John would recognize Padraig, but he never knew Anthony, so he would be the first one to speak. When Padden was close enough, Anthony called out to him.

"Hello there! Do you think you could help me? I just need a good pull, and I'll be off the sandbar here."

John told the young man he was a fool to be in

these waters if he hadn't known how to get himself about, but he turned his boat and headed toward an unknown fate.

Padraig was holding an oar, and just the sound of Padden's voice made him tighten his grip. Anthony whispered, "Not yet, Da, hold on; he will be here soon."

"You will have your revenge. Soon he will pay for the loss of your daughter and grandchild — he, the cause of their departure from Ireland.

"Soon you shall end your shame, and end the life of John Padden."

The Ballina Journal, And Connaught Advertiser.

THE BALLINA JOURNAL, MONDAY SEPTEMBER 17, 1888.

BALLINA, MONDAY 17, 1888.

ON Tuesday last Robert Mostyn, Esq., Coroner, held an inquest at Bangor on the body of John Padden. The circumstances surrounding the death were mysterious. He absented himself from his home on the 2nd, and his body was found in an upright position in about 10 feet of water on the 9th. The large discoloured mark on the shoulder showed that he must have come into contact with something previous to death. It transpired from the evidence that he had been subject to epileptic fits, and the doctor having certified that the death resulted from suffocation. A verdict accordingly.

RESEARCH

My great-grandmother, Katherine Walsh "Pad-den," arrived in Quebec, Canada, with her young daughter Mary Magdalen, my grandmother. Kate and Mary stayed with a Quaker family until such time as they could leave Canada for the United States. The people providing her a temporary home wanted to adopt Mary, but Kate would not part with her little girl. She and her little girl quickly and quietly entered the United States and Northeastern Pennsylvania. The Reilly family opened their home and hearts to their relatives from Ireland. Kate and Mary arrived in the small yet prosperous town of Pittston, and made their new home in the area of that city called "The Junction." Two rivers, the Lackawanna and the Susquehanna, joined there. But a more import-ant convergence in Pittston was that of three rail-way lines: The Wyoming, Lehigh, and Delaware. Pittston was the center for distribution of anthra-cite coal. It was a dirty business, but it employed many men.

It was here that Kate Walsh met and married Peter McFadden and had seven more children. She kept her past a secret and made the unearthing of her Irish roots very difficult after her death.

Mary Magdalen was too young when she left Ireland to have many memories of her past. She grew into a lovely young woman and learned quickly how to help her mother's growing family by working. She was hired as a domestic to live in the Fee household, as the mother of the house was quite ill. Mary spent her time in the kitchen; she was an excellent baker, often selling her bread at market in town. It was here she was to meet her future husband, Thomas Fee.

When she and Thomas were wed, they moved to a part of The Junction where Thomas was employed. The Coxton Yard was home to the roundhouse of the Lehigh Valley Railroad. As the family grew, they needed a larger home. They purchased one on the top of a hill overlooking the town — the "homestead" on Chapel Street. It was here Mary Magdalen and Thomas Fee raised eleven children — six sons and five daughters.

John Francis Fee, my father, was the youngest son.

The Fees were a proud Irish-American family. John spent countless hours and quite a bit of money searching for information on his Irish roots. From the distance of the United States, he relied upon the Family History Research Centres of County Sligo to find the birthplace of his grandmother Kate, as she was said to have been from County Sligo. But in all of my father's searching, there was not a "Katherine Walsh" to be found there. Nor was there a marriage certificate for Katherine Walsh and John Padden.

John Fee, my father, had more success in bringing to light information about his father's past rather than his mother's: My Grandfather, Thomas Fee, was born in Leeds, England. Both of his parents left Ireland while they were children around the time of the famine in 1847. The only knowledge we had was that they had lived in County Mayo, in the Parish of Kilbride.

In 1990, four years prior to my father's death, he

and my mother joined my husband and me in Ireland. Jason and I had gone there on our honeymoon in 1989 and from there continued on to reside in Portugal for several months, where Jason painted and presented a one-man show of his artwork at the American Embassy, Lisbon.

After this stay, we planned a reunion with my parents in Ireland. They arrived at Shannon Airport, where we met them in our rental car and drove them anywhere they wanted to go. My husband was to drive many miles and open many rusty cemetery gates in the next ten days. We searched for Kilbride — there were several in County Mayo alone. We stopped at many cemeteries, searching for the Fee name, without luck. We drove through much of County Mayo and made it as far as County Sligo before my father decided to head south to see more of the country.

We were not aware of it at the time, but my father had passed through areas of Ireland where the Fee family had lived (I was to find that cemetery in 2005). It was a grand trip, and I am proud to have been in an Irish pub and drink a "pint" with me own Da!

In the years following my father's death, I continued to search for evidence of the life Katherine Walsh had lived in Ireland. She was a mystery to me. And, as a woman, perhaps I wanted to know more about this brave, adventurous person of my own blood, who came across the Atlantic with a small child at her side, back when a trip of that nature was a dangerous one.

Knowing that she married a "Peter McFadden" shortly after arriving in Pennsylvania, I searched the Pennsylvania, Luzerne County, Marriage and Naturalization records and found the application for their marriage. Only she and her future husband would see this form. It would be kept in the courthouse records until, many years later, I was able to find it and view it. On the form, Kate had confirmed she had not been married prior to Peter McFadden — yet she used "Padden" as her last name. She also listed her mother's maiden name as "Newcomb," adding even more to the mystery. On her death certificate, her mother's maiden name was listed as "Day." I was finding it very difficult to find any more information. I came to realize that it would require me to go to Ireland to complete my work.

In Dublin, I began again in the National Library. Here, I had access to Tithe Applotment Books, Griffith's Primary Valuation, and Irish Civil Registration Indexes. The National Archives of Ireland hold the State Public Records — that is to say, any remaining after the mysterious fire of 1922. Records dating back to the thirteenth century were destroyed. It was also the year the Irish Free State was established, and the fire forever erased the records of the true Irish landowners, leaving only English landlords in their place.

While living in Westport, County Mayo, in the winter of 2004, I frequently traveled to the town of Castlebar, the location of the County Mayo Main Library. I had access to Kilmore Erris Parish Records and Griffith's Valuation of Tenements. I found a "Walsh" family in the Belmullet area, specifically South Inishkea, so Jason and I decided to take a drive.

We arrived in Belmullet and asked for directions to the parish priest's home.

I knocked on the door and was greeted by Father John McHale. I discussed with Father McHale my motivation for discovering the whereabouts of Katherine Walsh. I gave him all of the information I had gathered to date, including the application for marriage in Pennsylvania and her Death Certificate for the year 1944.

He promised to do some searching in the church records. It was a pleasant visit with the priest as he took the time to tell us of the story of Inishkea and its reason for now being deserted.

The impetus for this mass relocation was a tragic event — a natural disaster. In October of 1927, a violent storm did extensive damage to the homes on North and South Inishkea. But the greatest tragedy was the ten young fishermen who lost their lives. They had been out on the ocean in their *currachs*, fishing, when the storm came upon them suddenly, with gale-force winds and rogue waves, drowning them in the Atlantic

Ocean. With so much damage done, the government moved all the remaining inhabitants to the mainland of Belmullet.

We continued driving down to the very southern tip of the Mullet, Blacksod Bay. Here we came upon the ruins of another church and cemetery, so we stopped to explore. It was Saint Deirbhile's Church in Falmore. The belief was that, if you climbed through the arched window three times, you would never die from drowning. The windows are long gone, but there is still a doorway, so Jason and I did what we must — after all, we had future plans involving ships on the sea.

We returned to Westport, and, within a few days, I received a letter from Father McHale. In the baptismal records, he had found the birth of Katherine Walsh, dated May 22, 1864. The parents were Padraig Walsh and Ellen Lavelle; the Godparents were Bridget "Biddy" Geraghty and James Murphy.

Father McHale stated, "What is interesting is that Bridget Geraghty is also the Godmother of a Mary

Magdalen Walsh, baptized on September 6, 1881, daughter of Katherine Walsh." He added that he was only guessing, but, at that time, in the event that parents would "throw out" a child, custom and tradition dictated that the Godmother would be honor bound and have the responsibility to stand by and care for her Godchild." This is most likely what took place in Katherine Walsh's case.

The records also indicated that Katherine had siblings — one brother Anthony, born 1867, and two sisters: Rose, 1865, and "Honor," 1861. In the postscript, Father McHale said, "No one of this family married in my parish; subsequently, that gives me reason to believe they all immigrated to America."

Now I had my information, so I sent to Dublin for the birth certificate of Mary Magdalen Walsh, born September 5, 1881. When the form arrived, it carried the information I was looking for: Name of mother: Katherine Walsh; Place: Belmullet Workhouse. I had my proof. It was then that I applied for "citizenship by descent" in the Republic of Ireland.

On July 20, 2005, "Teresa Marie Fee" was entered into the Foreign Births Entry Book; I received my "birth" certificate and subsequent documentation of citizenship. I then applied for a passport, which was granted in October of that same year.

Continuing my research at the Castlebar Library, County Mayo, I read numerous old newspapers on microfilm. In *The Ballina Journal, Connaught Advertiser*, for the date September 17, 1888, I found an article concerning John Padden's suspicious death.

I contacted Mayo North Family History Research Centre with an inquiry about John Padden. They responded with this Death Record:

"John Padden, a bachelor from Shramore, Tullagh Bay, Parish of Erris, died on September 2, 1888, at the age of 50 years. The cause of death was accidental drowning and was registered by Robert Mostyn (Coroner). There was an inquest held in relation to this death on September 11, 1888."

That was where my research stopped, due to the speculative nature of the report of his demise. There were no further investigations other than the coroner's preliminary findings. I felt it may be wise to withdraw with honor!

With all of this information and knowledge, I then wrote the story of IRELAND'S MAGDALEN. What had begun as a family history project turned into an adventure and love story. I felt Kate loved John, although he changed her life dramatically. She used his name as her own, and the name for her daughter Mary Magdalen.

I discovered the complete truth of Katherine Walsh: though she took her story to her grave. Her own grandchildren would never know the depth and complexity of her life. Was there a suspicion in the family that she had never really been married in Ireland? Perhaps that is why it took a fourth generation to seek those answers. Having a child out of wedlock did bring shame upon the individual and the family. But I believe it was a child born of love: love a young girl felt to be true. The depth of the feelings she had for John Padden was passed to her daughter, by giving her his name: Padden.

I am proud to have come from such a strong, brave, adventurous line of women.

Teresa Marie Fee Goodman

IRELAND'S MAGDALEN

Archived in the permanent collections of the following libraries

IRELAND

NATIONAL LIBRARY OF IRELAND, Dublin

County Library of MAYO, Castlebar

Westport, Ballina, Belmullet

County Cork Library, Kinsale

WORLD BOOK TOUR 2014

"Spirit of Shanghai" Ship Captain Library

Panama City Library

Auckland, New Zealand

Sydney, Australia

Brisbane, Australia

Agnes Waters Library

Singapore

Hong Kong

UNITED STATES Libraries

Charleston, South Carolina

Wilkes-Barre, Pennsylvania

Pittston, Pennsylvania

Lancaster, Pennsylvania

Lititz, Pennsylvania

Burlington, New Jersey

Alexandria, Virginia

ACKNOWLEDGMENTS

UNITED STATES

National Archives, Washington, D.C.
United States Population Census 1910
Pennsylvania Division of Vital Records
Luzerne County, Pennsylvania: Marriage &
Naturalization Records

IRELAND

Ireland National Library, Dublin
Griffith's Primary Valuation of Tenements
National Church tithe/Tax Records
Mayo/Sligo Records of Births, Baptisms & Death
Registrations
Mayo North Family Heritage Center
Castlebar Library, County Mayo
Kilmore Erris Parish Baptismal Records
Belmullet Library/ Maps
The Ballina Journal & Connaught Advertiser
Newspaper articles:
*The Steamship DEVONIA
*Coroner report: September 1888
Bangor Civil Register of Deaths

ALCHEMY STUDIO, INC
Art & Design
Published by: Alchemy Studio Inc
Fine Literary Work
ALCHEMYSTUDIOINC.COM
JASON P. GOODMAN
On-site research assistant
Ireland Driver/Gate Opener

WINTERS Technical Art
Lititz, Pennsylvania

JOSH RIGGAN
Custom Finishes
IT Coordinator

Andrew Irwin
Technical Assistant
Westport Ireland

Katherine, Mary Magdalen, Joseph, Michael, Mary, Thomas Sr. & Thomas Jr.

Made in the USA
Columbia, SC
22 September 2019